GREEK MYTHOLOGY

GODS AND MEN

Stephanides Brothers'

GREEK MYTHOLOGY

GODS AND MEN

༽

Retold by Menelaos Stephanides
Drawings by Yannis Stephanides

Translation
Bruce Walter

SIGMA

GODS AND MEN

First edition 2000, 9th run 2020
Printed in Greece by "Fotolio", bound by G. Betsoris
© 2020 Dimitris M. Stefanidis
All rights reserved throughout the world

SIGMA PUBLICATIONS
42, Tebon Street, Ag. Dimitrios, 173 43 Athens, Greece
Tel.: +30 210 3607667, Fax: +30 210 3638941
www.sigmapublications.com
e-mail:sigma@sigmapublications.com

ISBN: 978-960-425-076-9

THE COURAGE OF ANCIENT GREEK THOUGHT

This volume, which begins with the birth of man, ends with the defeat of the gods. In choosing this order of events we have tried to show another aspect of Greek mythology. For apart from its poetic qualities, apart from the sometimes all-too-earthly characteristics of its gods, apart from its timeless and universal moral values, the mythology of the ancient Greeks has a crowning glory: that fearlessness of thought which was the distinctive fruit of ancient Greek philosophy and thought. When the chorus of the Oceanides cries out within the sacred confines of the theatre in its anguish for Prometheus: 'We have learned to hate traitors!' and that traitor is one of the twelve gods, or when 'treachery' is the word used to describe the execution of the orders of Zeus, ruler of gods and men, then we can see just how fearless and far-seeing was the thought that lay behind Greek myth.

CONTENTS

THE FIVE AGES OF MAN

The ancient Greeks, who lived long, long ago in the very earliest days of civilization, said that the immortal gods had created the human race not once, but five times.

The first race of all, they believed, was happy and god-like, so they named them the Golden Generation, and they called the times they lived in the Golden Age. Their life, they said, was one continual round of pleasures. They lived in perfect harmony with one another, free from cares and sorrows and untouched by war or natural disasters. They did not know what it meant to be tired, sick or in pain. Not even old age could wither them and they remained young and strong to the end. And when death finally did come to them, after many long and happy years, it stole upon them like a sweet sleep. As long as they lived they had all they could desire, for the earth was a true paradise and gave its rich fruits in abundance. Their placid flocks grazed peacefully in the green meadows, they lacked nothing and never knew hunger or want.

Although in the end they were all destroyed in punishment for the dreadful sins of the titan Cronus, the god who then ruled the world, when they died they became immortal spirits. They floated invisible over the face of the earth, punishing evil, repaying good deeds and upholding justice. This reward was given to them after their deaths by Zeus, when he in his turn became ruler of the world.

The Silver Generation was the next to inhabit the earth. How unlike the men of the Golden Age these newcomers were! Weak and foolish, they were incapable of managing their own affairs, let alone of helping others. For the first hundred years of their lives they were like helpless children in need of a mother's care, though even that was lacking often enough. And when they did finally grow up, their adult life was short, for they could not distinguish between good and evil, between what might help them and what might do them harm; and so they led lives filled with pain and sorrow. They had no appetite for work and no love for one another. They lived on what they could take by force and often ended up by killing one another in bloody quarrels. They disobeyed the immortal gods and never offered them sacrifices.

Angered by their evil deeds and by their lack of respect for the gods, Zeus sent them all to the joyless black depths of Hades, and by this punishment the Age of Silver was brought to an end.

Then Zeus, son of Cronus, created the third generation, the men of the Age of Bronze, or the sons of Pelasgus as they were sometimes called, after the name of one of their great kings.

The Age of Bronze bred men of mighty stature and invincible strength. They were terrifying in appearance and fearless warriors. They were clad in bronze and always ready to do battle. Their weapons were forged from bronze, and their dazzling armour was beaten from the same metal. Their tools were of bronze, and they even lived in brazen houses, for in those days man had not yet learned the use of iron. They did not plough the land, but lived by hunting and gathering wild fruit, and war was their constant companion. Yet although their mighty strength and stature were the gift of the gods, and not of their own creating, in the end they grew arrogant and swollen with foolish pride. Their looks became harsh and overbearing, and their hearts as hard as stone.

Yet however fearsome and strong they may have been, they did not escape their fate. Enraged by their insolence, Zeus despatched them all to the dark kingdom of the shades. And thus they, too, were cut off from the bright light of the sun.

Now a fourth generation came into the world, made glorious by Heracles, Theseus, Jason, Achilles and the whole great army of fearless heroes of Greek mythology. It was their deeds which gave the fourth generation its name: the Heroic Age.

Nobler and juster than their predecessors, the men of the Heroic Age were as fair as the gods themselves. The immortals often came down from Olympus and moved among them, sharing their joys and their sorrows. Many of their kings and the founders of their noble lines were fathered by some god, and the Olympians stood by them and protected them. Great and powerful cities rose and flourished during this period. The most renowned of them all was gilded Mycenae – for we have now reached the glorious age of Mycenaean civilization.

But nothing is eternal. A time came when even the generation of heroes was brought low. Countless warriors fell at the seven gates of Thebes, giving battle for the riches of King Oedipus, and more still died in the ten-year struggle before the walls of Troy – warriors who had sailed from every city of Greece in their galleys for the sake of fair Helen, daughter of Zeus. And when they had all been killed, Mycenae lost and Tiryns, Cnossus, Pylos and Iolchus and many another fair city, then great Zeus raised them up and took them to live far from the eyes of men in the Fortunate Isles, far, far away in the boundless ocean, in the most distant reaches of the world. In that remote place the Heroic Generation lead a life free from all pain and bitterness. There the earth yields its crops three times in a year, and its fruits are as sweet as honey.

With the passing of the heroes the mythical ages came to an end. The fifth generation which Zeus brought into the world was the human race, the workers of iron who still inhabit our abundant earth.

Life was difficult for this fifth generation. They had to work hard to survive, and their lives were beset with trials and problems. Even the gods seemed not to love them, for they withdrew to Olympus and from there showered disasters and bitter disappointments upon men's heads. Of course, they also dealt them out a few joys among all these sorrows, but the evil always outweighed the good and overshadowed their lives.

The men of the fifth generation lived with the memory of the race that had gone before them. The mythical era left a rich cultural heritage to its successors. Minstrels, poets and story-tellers went from city to city and from village to village recounting the heroic deeds of the lost generation at festivals, fairs and weddings. One of these was Homer, the blind ballad-singer who became the greatest poet of all times. Later, the immortal tragedies of Sophocles, Euripides and Aeschylus were to be performed in every city in Greece. And their themes were always borrowed from that unforgettable fourth generation, the mythical race of heroes.

These memories have come down to us over the centuries and are fresh even today – for there is one thing we should never forget, that Greek mythology deals above all with the exploits of the fourth generation, and when it died out, mythology came to an end.

But before we begin to speak of this age of renown we should look back at the one that came before it, to learn how the Age of Bronze vanished from the earth, and how the fourth generation of men came into the world.

PROMETHEUS
THE PROTECTOR OF MANKIND

As we have said before, mighty Zeus did not love the men of the third age, because they had grown proud and overbearing. For that reason he finally decided to overthrow them. It was not a sudden decision, however, and many things happened before Zeus finally made up his mind to take action. To take up the story from the beginning, it must be said that the men of the Age of Bronze had not always been bad. On the contrary, they had meant well at first and praised and worshipped the gods. Yet life was hard in those early days. Men had not yet learned to make fire and lived in the woods in rough shelters, caves or hollow trees.

And so they would have continued to live had it not been for Prometheus the titan, son of Iapetus. No other god loved mankind as he did. Prometheus dedicated his life to a great and noble goal: to stand at the side of mortal men and help them achieve a better life. He never counted the cost, although he knew beforehand how dearly he would eventually pay for the great love he felt towards mankind.

But, as he always said, "Nothing good and beautiful can be achieved without sacrifice."

His first good deed was to give men fire. He took it from the forge of Hephaestus and, holding it aloft like a lighted torch which banished the darkness, he brought it, running, to his friend man.

"A gift from the gods!" men exclaimed; and with the burning brand Prometheus had given them they lit undying fires everywhere to give themselves light and heat, to roast their food and to offer sacrifices to the gods. Yet this was not enough. Next Prometheus showed them how to work with fire. Soon they had built their first furnaces and began to smelt ore. They learned how to work bronze, silver and gold. From the bronze they made their tools, their household utensils, their weapons and everything else that they needed. They loved this metal, and wore bronze armour, and from then on became known as the bronze generation.

Prometheus' help did not stop here, however. Next he taught men how to tame the beasts of the field. It was thanks to him that mortals first learned to ride horses, drive the first chariots and cross the seas in the first ships. Prometheus even taught them to fight against disease. It was from him they learned to boil herbs over the fire to prepare medicines, and thus death was no longer quite the threat it had been till then. Prometheus even taught men to interpret oracles, to avoid ill-fortune and to overcome their difficulties. With his help new horizons opened for mankind. The gift of fire filled their minds with light, their hearts with warmth and their bodies with new vigour and strength. Now there was but one difference between gods and men: they were mortal while the gods lived for ever.

These developments did not meet with the approval of Zeus. For you see, the men of the Age of Bronze were mighty of stature, and once they had mastered the use of fire they were many times stronger than before. Now the ruler of gods and men began to fear them.

"It is all the fault of Prometheus," Zeus complained. "He is the one who gave them fire and helped them to become equal with the gods." The problem left him no rest, and in the end he began to heap misfortunes on mankind so that they would lose the power the son of Iapetus had given them.

But Prometheus boldly resisted Zeus' efforts.

"I cannot see mankind plunged into pain and sorrow," he said, and so he secretly continued to offer help and bring them new joys.

When the lord of the world heard what Prometheus had been doing, he was beside himself with rage.

"Tread softly, son of Iapetus," he threatened, waving his fist. "Defy me once more and I shall make you wish you had never been born."

"Learn this, son of Cronus," Prometheus replied. "I am not to be cowed by threats or broken by torture. You have forgotten the battles we once fought together and now you seek to frighten me into obedience. Do you not remember the battle of the Titans, where we struggled to save not only the gods, but man, too, from tyranny? I do not say that evil-doers should go unpunished, especially when they are powerful and lord it over whole cities or peoples. But why make all mankind suffer when they are only trying to improve themselves?"

With every such exchange of words the enmity between Zeus and Prometheus grew more bitter.

And at Sicyon things came to a head. Gods and mortals had gathered there together to decide which parts of the animals that men sacrificed should be offered to the gods and which should be kept by men. A great ox had been made ready for the ceremony. Prometheus was asked to divide it into two portions, and Zeus to decide which of them was to belong to the immortals and which to men.

Naturally, Zeus had no intention of giving away the best parts to mere mortals. Not that the gods had any need of the meat from the sacrifices, for they ate ambrosia and drank nectar, whose taste was sweet beyond men's imagining. What pleased the gods was the savoury smells which rose from the altar fires, and not the meat itself. Zeus, however, did not wish to do mankind any favours and he had already made up his mind: all the good meat would go to the gods and man would get nothing but the skin, the entrails and the bones.

Now Prometheus knew what Zeus had in mind, so he decided what he must do: he would trick the ruler of gods and men.

First he cut up the ox, picked out all the good pieces and heaped them on a great platter. Then he covered them all with the bloodied skin of the animal.

Next he filled another platter with the bones and carefully covered them with shiny white fat so that not a single bone could be seen.

When Prometheus had finished, he took the two platters and presented them to Zeus who stood waiting to give judgement, flanked on his right by all the gods of Olympus and on his left by the mortals, each side equally impatient to see which of the two he would choose.

As soon as the ruler of gods and men saw the platter draped with the blood-spattered hide, an expression of disgust crossed his face and he turned away his eyes. Next his glance fell on the second platter, and at the thought of the good meat which must lie beneath that gleaming white fat his mouth began to water.

Turning to Prometheus he said: "You may be the most intelligent of the gods, o son of Iapetus, but in this case you have divided most unfairly. So much the better. You have made my choice an easy one and I shall have no difficulty in deciding which portion should belong to the immortal gods."

"Choose as you will, mighty Zeus," replied Prometheus. "Your decision will be binding on gods and men alike."

Then Zeus pointed to the dish which gleamed with fat and said in a stern voice: "From now on this is the portion which shall belong to the gods; and that" – pointing to the other dish but not even deigning to look at it – "shall be the portion which belongs to men. That is my decision and nothing can ever change it!"

This last phrase had hardly escaped his lips when his face darkened. As if a suspicion had suddenly crossed his mind, he plunged his hands into the first dish, pushed the covering of fat aside – and exploded with rage. It was unthinkable! How could the lord of the world be fooled like this? Now mortal men would eat the sacrificial meat and for the immortal gods there would be nothing but the bones! And he himself had made the choice. What humiliation! However, the portions had been shared out now and nobody, not even Zeus himself, had the right to change them.

But there was something else he could do: he could withdraw the gift of the gods which Prometheus had offered mankind. He could take back their fire from heaven and deprive them of heat and light.

"We shall see if they like their meat uncooked," said Zeus to himself. "Now perhaps they will not think their crafty friend Prometheus has done them such a good turn, after all."

And that is just what Zeus did. He took back the gift of fire and hid it high on lofty Olympus, warning Prometheus with these words:

"As for you, son of Iapetus, beware of my wrath, for you know how harsh I am when I wish to punish."

But Prometheus was never one to be ruled by caution, and there was no power on earth that could stop him from helping the human race. And so, the very next day, he secretly brought the fire back down from Olympus, hidden in a hollow reed, and gave it once more to mankind. And from that day on, men have always cooked and eaten the meat of their sacrifices and offered only the white bones to the gods on their fragrant altars.

This time, however, Zeus' anger knew no bounds. A fearful punishment awaited Prometheus for stealing the gift of fire and taking it back to men. But first the lord of the world intended to punish mankind, and to do this he hatched a secret plan.

Zeus ordered Hephaestus, the blacksmith of the gods, to make him a woman out of clay. He told him to make her as beautiful as a goddess, to give her voice and movement, and to fill her eyes with divine enchantment.

So Hephaestus took earth and water and carried out his father's orders with wonderful skill.

The lord of the earth was delighted when he saw the result of Hephaestus' labours. It was just what he needed.

"I intend her as a gift for mankind," Zeus told the other Olympians, and they ran to deck her with gifts.

The goddess Athena wove her splendid gowns, brighter than sunbeams. The Three Graces decked her with lovely, gleaming jewellery. The Hours crowned her with a wreath of fragrant, snow-white flowers. The goddess of love, Aphrodite, bestowed irresistible charm upon her, and all the other gods and goddesses offered her some gift which would embellish her beauty and grace. For this reason the young woman was named Pandora, which means in Greek "all the gifts".

Endowed with so much charm and beauty, Pandora could have been a wonderful gift for mankind; but Zeus took care that it should be otherwise. He gave secret instructions to his son Hermes, and in obedience to his father's commands the crafty god taught her to speak sweetly but falsely, and gave her a sly and treacherous character.

Then Zeus ordered Hermes to take the girl as a gift for Epimetheus, Prometheus' brother, who lived on earth among

...The very next day, he secretly brought the fire back down from Olympus...

mortals. Unfortunately, the two brothers bore little resemblance to each other, for Epimetheus was not only slow-witted but weak-willed. Prometheus had often warned him never to accept any gifts from Zeus if he wanted to keep out of harm's way, but as soon as Epimetheus set eyes on Pandora's ravishing beauty he completely forgot his brother's advice and welcomed her with open arms. By the time he remembered Prometheus' warning it was too late, for he had already taken Pandora, the gift of Zeus, as his bride.

"Now I must be on my guard," he said to himself, thinking of a certain jar which stood in his house, a jar which Prometheus had carefully stoppered.

"Take care, Epimetheus," his brother had told him, "and make sure that this jar is never opened. For if it is, all manner of evils will be loosed upon the world." And from then on, Epimetheus had not only lost all desire to open the jar, but even to approach it.

Imagine Epimetheus' horror, then, when he found Pandora examining it curiously.

"Keep away from that jar, Pandora," he warned. "Prometheus gave instructions that it should never be opened. Take care, lest some great evil befall us all."

"Come now, why should I wish to open it," Pandora replied lightly. Yet in spite of her words, she could not drag her eyes from the intriguing object. Pandora's curiosity was aroused by most things that she saw, but above all by that jar, so carefully sealed and stoppered. And from the moment she was told to keep her hands off it, she was seized by such curiosity that she could not get a moment's rest.

"What can there be inside that jar and why am I not allowed to open it?" Again and again she asked herself this question until one day her inquisitiveness overcame her and, hardly able to wait until her husband had left the house, she rushed to the jar and opened it.

The moment she did so, she uttered a piercing scream of horror, for from out of the jar swarmed a horde of hideous monsters: Evil, Hunger, Hate and Sickness, Revenge, Madness and a host of kindred spirits. A terrible fear seized Pandora when she saw all these horrors spreading over the earth and, not knowing what else to do, she plucked up what courage was left to her, seized the stopper and sealed the jar once more. But in so doing she shut in the only spirit that had not yet emerged from its prison – and this was the spirit of Hope. And so everything came to pass exactly as Zeus had planned.

Thus all manner of evils were loosed upon the world, settling like a pestilence on city and village alike, drifting like a foul mist into every household and turning the life of men into a succession of bitter woes.

Prometheus watched all this in helpless grief, his heart as heavy as lead. Yet Zeus in his wrath had even worse in store for mankind, and Prometheus would be forced to look upon

the worst catastrophe that could befall them: their utter destruction.

DEUCALION'S FLOOD

When Pandora opened the jar and set free so many evils to prey upon the world, men grew wicked and cruel and ceased to respect the gods. It was then that Zeus finally decided to wipe them out. However, he needed some pretext for doing this, and the opportunity was given him by Lycaon, king of Arcadia, and his fifty sons.

Before the earth was overrun by evil, Lycaon, son of Pelasgus, was not only a good man but a worthy king, and there was no more faithful worshipper of Zeus among all the rulers of Greece. He built the first city in Greece, Lycosaura, and dedicated it to Zeus. He raised an imposing temple to

him, a place of pilgrimage where the ruler of gods and men
was worshipped in the manner that befitted him. He even
founded athletic contests, the Lycaia, in homage to Zeus. They
were the first such games in Greece.

Yet although the games were held in honour and praise of
Zeus, it was precisely over these that the lord of the world
found an excuse to destroy mankind.

The Lycaia were Panhellenic games. Every two years, that
is, athletes and visitors came from all over Greece and were
received with great hospitality. Lycaon even put his own palace at the disposal of these visitors. Hospitality was so highly
regarded in those days that the athletic contests were com-
bined with a festival in tribute to Xenius Zeus – "Zeus who
welcomes guests". For they all believed that it was he who
had laid down the sacred rules of hospitality.

But since that accursed day when Pandora had opened the
jar and evil had spread over the world, Lycosaura had forgotten what hospitality meant. No one treated strangers kindly
now, and so it came about that Lycaon, who had once honoured and worshipped Zeus above all men, now offered him
the most deadly insult. And as you may have guessed, the
incident occurred at those very games which were supposed
to be held in Zeus' honour.

Athletes and visitors from every region thronged the streets
of Lycosaura, for the Lycaian games were to begin next day.
Now, however, no one was willing to take them into their

homes as they had once done, and so the strangers wandered here and there like lost sheep and could find nowhere to sleep but in the streets and public squares.

Among the visitors was Zeus, disguised as an ordinary mortal. He wanted to see for himself the games and festival which were to be held in his name. But now he found every door barred against him and no one willing to give him food or shelter. In the end he decided to seek hospitality at the royal palace.

The stranger's commanding height and majestic appearance should have been enough to tell Lycaon who it was who stood before him. But no. Instead of this he cried out in fury:

"I have had enough of you foreigners. Why don't you sleep in the woods instead of dirtying our town?"

"The forests are for the wild beasts," replied Zeus, and at his words the steps of the palace were bathed in blinding light.

All those who were present, except Lycaon and his sons, knew by that sign that he who stood before them was none other than Zeus himself, and they fell on their knees and worshipped him.

"We do not worship strangers in the land of Pelasgus!" shrieked Lycaon in fury. "Bow the knee to your king, not to some foreigner!"

Then an old man stepped forward from the crowd and said in a stern voice:

"True, great king, we do not pay homage to strangers in

this place, but in the past the sons of Pelasgus always worshipped Xenius Zeus and offered hospitality to every stranger
that entered our gates. Now, however, we cast them out, and
I fear that some great evil will befall our city and yourself.
Receive this man we took for a stranger, for he has shown
that he is no mere mortal but Zeus himself. Honour him as
befits the ruler of the world, and prepare a splendid feast for
him."

"Enough, old man," replied Lycaon, "I will receive this
stranger. But do not presume to offer me advice on how I
should do so, for that is mine to decide."

With these curt words Lycaon granted the old man's plea.
He had no intention of honouring Zeus, however. His aim
was to humiliate him.

And what a method he chose!

He ordered his sons to cook Zeus the most revolting meal
that could possibly be imagined – and they served him up a
mixture of animal and human flesh!

Of course, Zeus immediately realized what kind of dish
had been set before him, and roared out in anger:

"So this is Lycaon! How dare he insult the ruler of the
world so shamelessly!" No, Zeus would certainly not tolerate
such treatment any longer! Beside himself with rage, he overturned the table and burned Lycaon's palace to the ground
with a thunderbolt.

"And now it is you who shall go and live in the forest," he

told Lycaon and his sons, flinging back their own words in their faces. And as he spoke they were transformed into the wild and ravenous beasts which have ever since been known in Greek as "lycoi", but which in English are called wolves.

Howling hideously, the beasts fled up into the dense forest behind the palace, up to Mount Lycaion, as it was afterwards called in their memory.

But Zeus' anger was not appeased by this punishment alone.

"So this is the famous human race!" he shouted in his fury. "Now let Prometheus look at them and admire their works! I shall not leave a single one of them on the earth. They shall perish, the guilty and the innocent alike. I will destroy them for all eternity, and he who loves them so shall be forced to look on before punishment falls on him, too – a greater punishment than god or man has ever suffered."

These were Zeus' words. Yet who had sent Pandora to earth? Who was responsible for the evils which now plagued the world? Who was to blame for the sorry state to which mankind had been reduced? Zeus considered none of these things as he took his decision: he would drown the human race in a mighty flood, and along with it every living creature upon the earth.

Standing before Lycaon's upturned table, he called the wet South wind to his side and bid it journey far out to where the titan Oceanus stretches wide and boundless, and there to gather cloud upon heavy cloud, bursting with the waters of mighty

Oceanus, and then, blowing hard, to drive them quickly back to the mountains and the plains of the world.

Soon, heavy black clouds covered the whole earth. On and on they came until the entire sky was one vast expanse of black and all nature was clouded over.

Suddenly, sky and earth alike were lit up by a dazzling flash, and an ominous clap of thunder shook the whole world, echoing and re-echoing like a harbinger of doom. There followed a deadly silence, heavy with fear. Then suddenly disaster struck. Amid a frightful turmoil of lightning and thunderclaps there began a downpour which seemed like a thousand waterfalls tumbling from the heavens. Down teemed the rain the clouds had gathered from the boundless ocean, in an inexhaustible and endless deluge.

Soon water covered the plains and the heights were flooded, yet the cataclysm continued unabated until all nature was one vast sea from horizon to horizon and even the high mountains were inundated. Now only lofty Olympus and the twin peaks of Parnassus still showed above the waters.

Where men had once tilled the fields, fish now swam, and where man's flocks had once grazed, schools of dolphins now sported. By rights, not a single human being should have survived the catastrophe. And yet it was not so. For once more Prometheus had thwarted Zeus' plans and saved the human race from total destruction.

Prometheus had a son, Deucalion, who was king of

Phthiotis, and he had warned him of the impending flood and told him what he must do to save himself and his family.

As soon as he had received his instructions, Deucalion set to work. Hundreds of venerable oaks and straight and lofty cypress trees fell to the blow of his axe. For Deucalion was building an ark, a great vessel which would hold not only his family but a host of animals as well.

With the eager and untiring help of his wife, Pyrrha, and their children, Deucalion's work went forward briskly. The keel was carved from thick tree-trunks, the ribs slotted into it and the decks nailed on with wooden pegs. The seams were carefully caulked with pitch. Finally the roof was added, and that, too, was given a good coating of tar.

When all was ready, the animals began to go into the ark. They all arrived and went on board of their own accord, one male and one female of every beast and bird in the world, from the proud lion to the crawling snake. They offered one another no harm but went quietly to their appointed places as the wise titan Prometheus had ordained.

With the help of Pyrrha and their children, Deucalion stocked the ark with sufficient food to last them all, man and beast, for many days.

By the time all was ready, the skies were dark with clouds, so Deucalion ordered his wife and children to get on board without delay, and when they had done so, he and his eldest son, Hellen, mounted the gangplank and pulled it up behind

them. It was clear that the weather was not going to wait, and hardly had they made the hatches fast than the storm broke.

Soon the rising waters had lifted the ark from the earth. For nine days and nine nights it drifted at the mercy of the

tempest while Pyrrha and Deucalion listened anxiously to the drumming of the seemingly endless rain. But on the morning of the tenth day, a sudden bump told them that the ark had found land once more. Deucalion ran to open a window. The rain had stopped, but a sheet of water stretched to the horizon in all directions, save for a little islet crowned by twin peaks where the ark had come to rest.

Deucalion knew the place.

"We are on the summit of Mount Parnassus," he exclaimed. "I believe the worst is over, but before we go ashore we must make sure the weather is not going to turn stormy again." Then he released a dove. In those days everybody knew that these birds have an unerring instinct for the weather, and so if it returned in alarm, it would mean that the storm was about to break once more and they should not leave the safety of the ark. But the dove perched at the open window for a moment, looked around at the weather and then flew joyfully to the mountain peak.

When he saw this, Deucalion put all the animals ashore and then stepped out onto dry land himself, followed by Pyrrha and their children.

Thus Prometheus saved the human race and all life was not washed from the face of the earth.

Now though it was believed in Greece that Deucalion's ark came to land on the slopes of Mount Parnassus, the Greeks of southern Italy said that the waves had carried the ark as far as their lands, and that it had finally come to rest on Mount Etna. In the eastern lands, on the other hand, another version of the myth prevailed, especially in the years following Alexander the Great's conquests. In those parts it was believed

that the wind carried Deucalion's ark to the cedar-clad summit of Mount Lebanon, and until the coming of Christianity,
the spot where the ark was believed to have come to rest was
a place of pilgrimage throughout the East, so widespread was
the myth of Deucalion and his ark in those far-off days.

But let us return to Deucalion, still huddled with his family near the mountain-top. Their first act on coming ashore
had been to pray to Hera, wife of Zeus. They were still afraid
to offer up their prayers to Zeus himself lest he fly into an
even greater rage and blast them all with a bolt of lightning.
Only Hera could calm him and soften his anger.

"Great queen of the skies," said Deucalion and Pyrrha,
"look what evil has befallen the world. Beg Zeus to make the
waters withdraw, and we shall be grateful to you for ever."

Hardly had they spoken when the mountain split asunder
at their very feet and a bottomless gulf opened which began
to swallow the waters with a great roar. Soon the boundless
seas which had surrounded them were gone, and the mountains and plains were visible once again. Then the great rift
closed. Where it had been, however, a crack remained in the
earth, and over this spot Deucalion and Pyrrha built a temple
to the goddess Hera. Then, having offered up their thanks for
her help, they loaded their few belongings on an animal and
made their way down to the plains.

Not a soul could be seen anywhere. Desolation and decay
surrounded them: ruined houses, uprooted trees, boulders and

mud lay all around.

With heavy hearts they drew to a halt before the river Cephissus.

"We are the only ones who were saved," said Deucalion. "Come, let us build an altar and give thanks to almighty Zeus for granting us our lives."

When they had done this, and begged Zeus to help them, the god Hermes appeared, sent by the ruler of the world himself. And this is what he told them:

"Mighty Zeus was so pleased when he heard you offering up your thanks that he sent me to tell you that you may ask what you will of him, and he gives his word that your wish will be granted, whatever it may be."

"We would like the earth to be filled with people once again," replied the couple in unison.

Then Hermes hastened back to Olympus, and when Zeus heard what they had requested, he sat in thought for a while and then finally said:

"So let it be. I am no longer angry with men. Now the time has come for Prometheus to pay." And to show how seriously he meant these words, he sent Themis herself, the goddess of law, to instruct Deucalion and Pyrrha. She told them:

"If you throw behind you the bones of your great mother, everything you have asked for shall be granted."

But Deucalion and Pyrrha did not have the same mother, for they were man and wife, not brother and sister, and for a

...They began to throw them back over their shoulders...

while they were at a loss. Then, suddenly, Deucalion's face lit up. He had grasped the meaning that lay behind Themis' words and he cried:

"Olympian Zeus means that we should throw behind us the bones of Mother Earth, for it is she who is the great mother of us all."

"Yes, she is the mother of all things," replied Pyrrha, "and these pebbles are her bones."

Then they both stooped and picked up the stones that lay on the river bank and began to throw them back over their shoulders.

Immediately they did so, the stones that Deucalion threw became men, and those thrown by Pyrrha turned into women.

Thus the earth was filled with people once again, and thus it is that the ancient words for 'stone' and 'people' are almost the same.

And so the fourth generation of men came into the world.

Deucalion had many children by Pyrrha, and their descendants were all the renowned heroes of Greek mythology.

By their mighty deeds they brought glory to the generation which so justly bears their name: the Heroic Age; and however much the lord of the world may have hated Prometheus, fate so ruled that in the veins of that glorious breed of heroes Prometheus' blood should flow: for all the Greeks are said to spring from Hellen, son of Deucalion and grandson of Prometheus. And that is why the Greeks are also called the Hellenes.

Hellen succeeded to his father's throne and ruled in Phthiotis. He had three sons: Aeolus, Dorus and Xuthus. From Aeolus the Aeolians are descended, from Dorus the Dorians, and from the sons of Xuthus, Ion and Achaeus, sprang the Ionians and the Achaeans.

Thus, so mythology would have us believe, the four races which make up the people of Greece were not only descended from the progeny of Prometheus, but even took their names.

Yet Zeus' hatred for Prometheus was not quenched by the waters of the flood. His wrath had been turned aside from man only to be directed even more fiercely against the proud titan. Now Zeus could no longer wait to punish Prometheus for daring to go against his will and for giving the gift of fire to the human race.

Prometheus knew that he would not escape the harsh punishment Zeus was preparing for him, and so he went secretly to find Athena and speak with her. Knowing how much the blue-eyed goddess loved mankind he told her:

"A terrible fate awaits me, Athena. I shall be bound with unbreakable chains and suffer horrible tortures for all eternity. However, it is not this which I fear most, but that mankind should be left without a helper."

"The sufferings you are doomed to bear are enough for you. Do not torture yourself over man's fate as well," replied Athena in a determined voice. "I will do all that you bid me and more."

Then Prometheus sat with the goddess and taught her architecture, astronomy, mathematics, shipbuilding, metalworking, medicine and many other arts so that she in her turn would be able to teach them to mankind.

"Perhaps it is better this way," said Prometheus when he was through. "Zeus loves you dearly, and he will not stand in your way. Besides, you know how to win him over, and I certainly do not."

"Never fear, brave titan," replied Athena. "I shall not fail you. And now, be of good courage."

Truly, of all the immortals Athena was the only one who could carry on the work of Prometheus. Her determination to succeed gave new strength to the great friend of mankind. His mind set at rest, he surveyed the green and fertile earth and imagined it as it would become, made more beautiful still by the work of man. Happiness filled his soul, and in a fearless voice he said:

"Now let Zeus do his worst to me. I am ready."

THE HIDEOUS SUFFERINGS OF
PROMETHEUS

*"Of all those who have suffered for humanity, the most saintly
figure is that of Prometheus", a great philosopher once said.*

His chains rattling harshly in the bleak wilderness, the titan Prometheus, son of Iapetus, walked over the jagged stones,
his limbs shackled with unbreakable bonds. A terrible punishment lay in store for him, because he had dared to steal
fire from heaven and give it to mankind, in defiance of the

will of Zeus.

And now the great ruler of gods and men had ordered him to be bound with heaven-forged chains and nailed to a rock in this wild place for all eternity.

Yes, for ever! This was Zeus' decision and everyone knew it could not be changed, for the lord of the universe never went back on his word.

Unbowed, his head held high, Prometheus mounted the rock. He knew what fearful tortures awaited him in that place, although his only crime had been his deep love for mankind. Heavy fetters hung from his wrists and ankles, their loose ends firmly grasped by a giant slave, a grim-faced servant of Zeus, who scowled angrily at the fearless titan. Violence was his name. Behind him, with melancholy face and bent head, trailed Hephaestus, the blacksmith of the gods. His features were drawn with anguish for Prometheus and he cursed the skills he had learnt, now that he must turn them against his best friend and nail him to the rock. Worst of all, he knew that far from being punished for any evil deed, Prometheus was paying for the good he had done mankind. The sorrow of Hephaestus weighed more and more heavily upon him as they approached their goal.

Now they had arrived. They had passed through Thrace, crossed over the river Istros, traversed the whole of Scythia, and before them lay the towering peaks of the Caucasus, looming over the wind-tossed sea. No living soul had ever set foot

in that desolate wilderness of jagged rocks and yawning preci-
pices. Not a blade of grass had ever sprouted in its lonely
wastes. Since time immemorial its heights had been swept by
the wild winds and its bleak coasts battered by the thundering
waves of the stormy Black Sea.

At the foot of a towering rock-face Violence drew to a halt
and with his lips twisted in a snarl of malice said,

"Here's the very place! This bare crag catches the full force
of the wind. Here, the tempests and the snowstorms of winter
will lash his body ceaselessly and the summer sun will burn
him to a cinder. Let him be nailed here for ever to strike fear
into the hearts of those who think they can defy the will of
Zeus!"

And then, fixing Hephaestus with an angry glare, he
shouted,

"Come on! What are you waiting for? Get to work at once!
Bind him fast to the rock so he can never free himself. Then
drive this nail straight through his chest to hold him upright
so that he won't even be able to kneel or lean over sideways
to sleep. Let him not have a moment's rest from his tortures.
How glad I am he is immortal, for thus not even death will
ever put an end to his sufferings – the villain!"

Hephaestus gave a deep groan and replied,

"I do not know which of us is a villain. Perhaps you are,
perhaps I am – but Prometheus is not. Oh son of Iapetus, my
heart bleeds for you, but I cannot disobey my father's orders.

I must now bind you fast to this rock. And for what? For giving man everything you had to give."

"Watch your words, blacksmith!" shouted Violence in a threatening tone. "Don't waste your pity on this thief."

"Your tongue's as ugly as your looks", replied Hephaestus. "It's time you learned that stealing and giving don't mix!"

"If the lord of the world says he's a thief and a villain, then that's what he is. What Zeus thinks, we must think, too. For no one in this world is truly free but he alone. And you know perfectly well that whatever freedom is given to us, we owe to him."

"Free to do evil!" retorted Hephaestus. "Free to obey blindly! Is that what you call freedom? But there is one among us with a spirit brave and unfettered beyond compare – one who is freer than Zeus himself, even though he be in chains!"

"Prometheus, you mean? Are you mad? If Zeus heard you, he'd blast us both with a thunderbolt – and I don't see why I should pay for your treacherous ramblings. He's a thief and a villain. Zeus said so, and that's that. Now get on with it. Nail him up and let's be done with him!"

"No, no!" replied Hephaestus. "If there is any light, any liberty in this world, they stand here in chains before us. I would rather never have been born than be doomed to crucify with my own hands the fairest of all the gods. Only one hope sustains me: that in the end truth will triumph – for however it is twisted and abused it will be revealed at last."

"That's enough!" shouted Violence, brandishing his fist. "If you don't watch out you may suffer the same fate yourself one day. Perhaps only that would put some sense into your head and make you realise the value of what little freedom is left to us!"

"So now Violence presumes to teach us about freedom!" retorted Hephaestus. "Understand this, fellow: I don't care what fate I suffer!" But as he spoke these words his face grew even sadder and he added,

"Yet whether I care about my own skin or not, there is one thing I cannot do, and that is to go against my father's will and avoid the fate that has been meted out to me."

For a while there was a tense silence. Violence's looks grew darker and darker and it was clear that he could hardly contain his impatience. For a long time Hephaestus ignored him, then, finally, and with a deep groan, he picked up his hammer and began work.

"Strike harder!" shouted Violence. "Drive the chains deep into the rock!"

The solid rock rang and all the Caucasus shuddered beneath the fearful blows of the blacksmith of the gods. His hammering echoed through the world like thunder.

Now Prometheus was bound to the rock with iron chains so strong that not even Hephaestus himself could break them.

"And now the nail!" cried Violence. "Plunge it into his chest and pin him to the rock!"

And that, too, was done. The whole mountain groaned as
if the lifeless rock itself were in agony, yet not a sound escaped the lips of the unflinching titan. Proud and erect, he
endured the frightful torture to the end, and all the while his
gaze was fixed upon some distant horizon, far, far away beyond the storm-tossed sea – where men lived and worked.

When the task was done, Violence looked up at him and
snarled,

"Now curse Zeus how you will! Here in this wilderness he
neither hears you nor wishes to hear. But take this advice from
me: if you want to rob the gods, then give what you steal to
some immortal, and not to men; for only a god might some
day be able to free you from these bonds. There is no man
alive could ever break the chains that bind you."

Violence spoke these words little guessing that some day
just such a thing might happen: that a great hero would at last
be born who possessed exactly the power he spoke of, and
would use it to smash the heaven-forged chains that held the
fearless titan.

"And now let us be on our way," concluded Violence. "Now
he's strung up here, perhaps he'll recognize the power of Zeus
at last and repent his evil deeds. But even so it will do him no
good, for what the gods decide can never be undone."

And with these words he turned his steps towards home.
The lord of the world could have no complaint with Violence.
He had made sure that a good, sound job had been done. Zeus'

greatest enemy would hang here in eternal agony.

His head bowed and his face dark with grief, Hephaestus stood apart. Then he raised his eyes for one brief look at mankind's greatest friend. He gazed into his eyes and saw there, not suffering, but unbendable determination: never to give in to injustice, never to bow to force, even if subjected to the most horrible and endless torture ever known to gods or men.

Then Hephaestus lowered his eyes once more and turned to leave. As he trudged slowly away, his head downcast, the dry, defiant eyes of the painracked titan still seemed to shine into his own, and two heavy tears trickled down his cheeks.

Soon Prometheus was utterly alone. And then the silence of that deserted spot was rent by a deep groan wrenched from the pierced breast of the chained titan. Only now that his tormentors were gone would he deign to reveal his agony.

"Oh Earth and Sky and bright Sun who sees all," he cried. "Look what a god suffers, nailed to this rock by his own kind for a crime that is no crime at all. 'You stole fire for mankind,' Zeus told me. Yes, I did! And I knew what punishment awaited me, for I can see into the future. Yet I did not hesitate. And whatever horrors I have yet to bear, my resolve will not waver. I will endure humiliation and unending torture until justice grows to mighty stature and spreads over the whole earth."

Having said these words he fell silent. He seemed to hear something, a sound that resembled the soft rustling of windblown leaves. And soon he saw what it was. The goddesses of the waters were coming towards him, the Oceanides, the daughters of white-haired Oceanus, the great titan who enfolds the whole world in his embrace.

They drew near.

A cry of horror broke from their lips when they beheld the hideous sight. Afterwards they stood motionless and dumb, unable to believe the evidence of their own eyes. Finally, the eldest of them broke the silence:

"We heard the echoes of the hammer-blows and came here with our father's blessing to try to ease your pain, unhappy Prometheus. But what we see here is horrible beyond belief. Our minds cannot grasp what our eyes tell us."

"O daughters of great Oceanus, most faithful of friends," replied the titan. Wherever there is suffering, your kind hearts hasten your footsteps to the spot. And now you see to what torture Zeus has condemned me – chained upright to this rock like a sentry no one would ever wish to relieve."

"Our hearts bleed for you, Prometheus," they replied. "For you are the light and the hope of mankind. But now Zeus rules the world harshly, and punishes harshly, too – whether justly or unjustly we do not yet know. Yet even if you were at fault, we do not believe that any crime could deserve such a punishment."

"It could."

"Then tell us what terrible deed you committed."

"I saved the human race when Zeus wanted it destroyed!"

"But that was a wonderful thing to do, not a crime!" the Oceanides cried.

"I stole fire from Zeus and gave it back to mankind!"

"But even so, you did man a great service, and still did no harm to the gods."

"I taught mortals to heal their sicknesses, and I put hope into their souls!"

"Alas, what a kind heart they have nailed to this rock!" sobbed the Oceanides when they heard these words.

"I taught men arts and sciences. I showed them how to read and write. I taught them how to build houses, and I gave them the warmth of the hearth."

"But how could you be punished for all these kind deeds?"

"For these and many other acts of kindness towards man, you see how I am punished. But mark my words. If I had done some great evil, perhaps I would never have been punished at all. The unjust reserve their harshest punishments for those who fight against injustice."

"Alas, you speak true, unhappy Prometheus. If only it were not so. But look in the sky over yonder. Someone seems to be coming."

They looked carefully. Soon they could make out on the horizon a winged chariot flying between the clouds. It was drawn by a snow-white pegasus. The winged horse was carrying their father's familiar chariot towards them. White-

haired Oceanus, son of Uranus the sky and mother Earth, had
flown here from the farthest reaches of the world in this difficult hour to help his friend. Humble and pure of heart, Oceanus
had gone to live in solitude far away from Olympus because
he could not bear to see the injustice which ruled in the world;
but now that his good friend was in trouble, he felt that he had
to come to his aid.

Oceanus' heart was wrung with grief when he saw the great
benefactor of mankind hanging from the rock.

"Ah, what is this I see?" he cried. "Why is there so much
injustice in the world?"

"Do you remember, Oceanus, how once we both helped
Zeus?"

"I do indeed!" retorted the white-haired titan. "And I am
off to Olympus this very moment! I am going to remind Zeus
of our old friendship. I know how to soften his heart and make
him set you free – but learn to keep out of harm's way, for
you know that though Zeus rules us harshly, none may challenge his rule."

"You have described the situation exactly," broke in
Prometheus, "and for that reason, do not go to see him. Beware, Oceanus, lest some ghastly fate befall you, too. For
instead of softening his heart you may work him into a worse
rage. Nothing will ever make him change the hatred he feels
for me."

"I shall go," replied Oceanus. "You must be saved and this

injustice must be righted. I do not care if I endanger myself."

"I have always known what a true friend you were. And as we know, it is in times of need that one can count on one's true friends. I am grateful to you, Oceanus, but I will not let you run such risks on my behalf. You will not make Zeus change his mind, I say – and besides, it is not right for you to go begging injustice for mercy. I would not want such a thing. Go now – and if you disagree with me, I do not wish to hear you, for my mind is made up."

The white-haired titan's face fell as he heard these words, for now he finally realised that there was nothing he could do to help and that his shackled friend was beyond all persuasion. With a heavy heart, he climbed back into his chariot, tugged on the reins, and was drawn up into the sky by his broad-winged pegasus.

"Do not leave him there alone!" he cried to his daughters as his chariot rose from the earth. And then he was gone.

Plunged into despair now that all hope was lost, the Oceanides began to lament the terrible fate which had overtaken the chained titan.

"It is not only Greece which mourns for you, great titan," they wailed. "All over the world men weep and suffer with you: the craftsmen of Asia and the slim virgins of Colchis, all the tribes of the Scythians, the warlike hosts of Arabia, and those who man the mighty fortresses on the jagged peaks of the Caucasus."

Then they remembered Atlas, the mighty brother of Prometheus, who bore on his shoulders for all eternity the crushing weight of the globe.

"Even his sufferings cannot be compared with yours, fearless helper of mankind. No punishment has ever been devised that could be compared with your eternal agony."

The Oceanides continued to bewail the titan's fate, but Prometheus remained silent. Suddenly, however, he raised his eyes, looked at the daughters of his greatest friend and said,

"It is not exhaustion or pain which prevent me from speaking, but the memories and thoughts which flood my mind; for I no more expected than you that Zeus would punish me in such a fashion. There was a time when he and I were the dearest friends – and what is more, we were friends in a great cause. In those days we both saw the injustice which reigned around us. We saw how lawless was the reign of Cronos, the titan who ruled the world in those days. We saw how his injustice brought all manner of evil into the world – vile monsters like Madness, Hunger, Hate, Sickness and War. We watched them spread over the earth, work their way among men and turn the whole world into a living hell. It was then that we decided to cast Cronos from the throne of the gods and prepared ourselves for the great war against him and the other titans. Zeus knew that he could count upon his brothers help, but this was not enough. I helped him with all the powers at my disposal. First I found him allies: my wise mother, Themis; your father, great Oceanus; the goddess Earth, mother of all creatures; and finally the Cyclopes, who gave him their thunder. And I, like all the others, fought at his side for the whole ten years of that fearful war until the Battle of the Titans was ended and Zeus emerged victorious. Then, one by one, I rounded up all the monsters that the reign of Cronos had loosed upon the earth and I shut them up in a great earthenware jar. And so that they should not escape, I gave it to my brother Epimetheus to guard. Then I began to help mankind. To rescue them from their misery I gave them the gift of fire. Zeus flew into a rage. Why? What had mankind done to harm him? Was he afraid of them, perhaps? I do not know. Whatever the reason, Zeus' attitude towards men changed and he became fixed in his determination to do them harm. The trouble started with the sacrificial ox at Sicyon. Zeus did not want men to eat meat, but only to burn it as an offering to the gods upon their altars. I stopped him from having his way. Then he took away my gift of fire so that they would not be able to cook the meat I had won for them. I stole the fire back from Zeus and returned it to mankind. We became enemies. By now Zeus had but one aim: to punish me. To spite me, he sent Pandora to earth, and she opened the jar in which I had shut up all those horrible monsters after the Battle of the Titans. The whole swarm of them spread over the earth once more. And when Zeus saw the depths men had sunk back into as a result, he sent down a great flood upon them to wipe out the human race for ever. Again I thwarted him, by saving Deucalion and Pyrrha. I could tell you a lot more, but the little I have said is enough. Now you understand why I am hanging from this rock with a nail driven through my chest. I did not have the art to fob men off with delusions and promises of eternal bliss. I merely enlightened their minds, made their lives more bearable and softened the pains of their earthly existence. And for doing that I gladly bear this punishment and would endure a worse!"

"Ah, Prometheus! You showed great love for the human race, but you took no thought at all for yourself."

"That is the way I was born," replied Prometheus, "and that is how I was destined to act."

"While the destiny of Zeus is to rule for ever," said the Oceanides.

"Do not say that," the titan retorted. "You do not know everything that is written by the Fates."

There were many such things which Prometheus could see, for he was the son of Themis, the goddess with the greatest power of prophecy of all the Olympians. The Oceanides knew this and so they asked,

"Have the Fates anything written for Zeus that he should be afraid of?"

"Only I know that," replied Prometheus. "But it is not yet time to speak. I shall not save Zeus as long as he rules un-

justly; and by keeping my secret I shall one day bring him to
his senses, and then I shall escape from my bonds."

"Ah, if only you could be free today!" they cried. "But
how can such a thing ever come about if these chains are so
strong that even he who forged them cannot break them?"

The Oceanides spoke like this because they did not know
there was to come a day when a hero would be born who had
the strength to smash the unbreakable chains which bound
the fearless titan!

But Prometheus replied from his rock,

"One day I shall be freed, that much I know. But before
that time comes, countless years will pass, for he who shall
break these bonds shall be long in coming. And until then I
shall suffer tortures such as no living creature has ever known.
But what do I see? Unhappy Io is coming this way. She could
never imagine that it is to be one of her distant descendants
who will be my rescuer."

As he spoke, the sky was filled with the heart-rending bellow of a cow in pain. It was Io who was making this terrible
noise. She had once been a lovely princess of Argos, but now
she was transformed into a miserable, suffering heifer foaming at the mouth, scratched and bloodied and running like a
thing possessed to escape the venomous bites of a giant horse-
fly. We have spoken in another volume of the agonies Io endured when Hera vented her wrath upon the unlucky princess. The poor girl had been pursued half way across the world,

and now she found herself in the Caucasus.

As soon as she came upon Prometheus hanging from the rock she stopped in her tracks, struck dumb by the dreadful sight. "The poor fellow must have committed some dreadful crime to be tortured so horribly," thought Io, "if I who have done nothing suffer such pangs."

But then, so racked was she by her own pain, that she lifted her head in despair and cried out with all the strength left to her,

"Lord Zeus! Why do you leave me to suffer like this? Why don't you strike me down with a thunderbolt and burn me to ashes? Why don't you open the earth to swallow me? Why not make me food for the fishes rather than force me to endure such pain?"

"O daughter of Inachus, on whom the wrath of Hera falls unjustly..." the titan's voice addressed her.

"Who are you, unfortunate creature? And how do you know my father's name and the fate which has befallen me?"

"I am he who made a gift of fire – or stole it, if you prefer. Put it how you will."

"You are Prometheus, the great benefactor of mankind!" cried Io.

"And that is why I am nailed to this rock and bound with unbreakable chains. Now you see that there are even worse sufferings than your own. Patience is the best medicine for pain."

..."You are Prometheus, the great benefactor of mankind!"
cried Io...

"Alas, if only I had your strength of will I could endure these sufferings and worse. But I can bear the torture no longer and I have only one thing left to ask: that I may fall dead this very instant."

"The strength you speak of can be found, and you, too, will acquire it when you learn that there will be an end to your sufferings and that your life in this world is not without purpose."

"O Prometheus!" cried Io. "You know all, for you can see into the future, too. But is it possible that my life can serve any purpose?"

"You will be astonished by what I have to tell you, but listen: it is through your offspring that I hope to gain my freedom!"

Io was staggered when she heard these words. Her mind could not grasp the possibility that she might one day have children and that one of their descendants would be so mighty that he would be able to break those heaven-forged chains! However, the rock-bound titan's words gave her new strength, so Io plucked up her courage and said.

"If I understand you rightly, you foresee that one day my horrible wanderings will come to an end and I shall become a human being again. Speak, I beg you, and tell me where and when my sufferings will cease."

"In Egypt," replied Prometheus, "where the mighty river Nile pours into the sea. It will take you a long time, you will wander far and wide and you will endure many more misfortunes before you reach Egypt. But there you will meet with Zeus, and he will turn you into a woman once more.

Io received the fearless titan's prophetic words with joy.

"I give you my thanks, Prometheus," she said, "and somehow I shall find the courage that I need. But tell me, what did you mean when you said that it was through my offspring you hoped to gain your freedom? For though your words have given me new hope and joy, I still cannot understand them clearly"

"I will tell you everything if you wish," replied Prometheus. "You will bear a son by Zeus after he rests his hand upon your head in distant Egypt and restores you to your former shape. The child you will bear shall be called Epaphos, because it was conceived through a mere touch. He will become the first king of Egypt, and his descendants will be a great race of heroes. From this breed a hero shall one day spring so mighty that even these chains will not be able to resist his strength. Heracles will be his name. But I, alas, must wait centuries for his birth."

Prometheus had hardly finished speaking when Io let out a pitiful bellow of pain. She sprang into the air and immediately took to flight. The fearsome horse-fly had once more driven its poisonous dart into her flank and the unfortunate Io was soon lost to sight as she fled over the jagged rocks.

"How wise was he who said the weak should never get

entangled with the strong," sighed the Oceanides. "For if the mighty are not corrupted by their wealth, their pride in their glorious heritage will ruin them."

When he heard these words, the chained titan shouted angrily,

"However proud Zeus is, a day will come when he finds his own hands bound in the frightful chains of slavery!" As he went on, Prometheus' voice rose in such fury that the whole Caucasus re-echoed: "There will come a time when he finds himself thrown from his high and airy palaces to the darkest depths of Tartarus. For Zeus himself will be the ancestor of the fearsome opponent who will cast him out of Olympus! There is only one way for him to save himself, and that is to learn the great secret. But that he shall never do, for there is but one person in the world who knows it, and that is I. Yes, Zeus! Now you are seated in splendour on the throne of the gods, but when you are thrown from the heights of your glory and tumbled, broken, into the dark depths, then you will realise the gulf that separates dominion from slavery!"

Terror seized the Oceanides when they heard the fearless titan's dreadful threat echoing from shore to shore.

"Prometheus!" they cried, "what are you saying? Are you not afraid that an even worse fate may befall you now?"

"If I feared the consequences of my deeds I should be sitting on Olympus now," retorted the titan. "But I have never been one to tread warily."

"They are wise who know when the must bow their heads."

"When they must, yes – but never in the face of tyranny!"

But at that very moment the winged god Hermes shot from the skies like a bolt of lightning. Zeus had sent him to learn the meaning of the titan's words.

Giving Prometheus a threatening look he shouted,

"You crafty, foul-mouthed thief! Stop speaking in riddles and tell me in plain words: who will cast lord Zeus from his throne, and what is this "great secret" which could save him? The mighty ruler of the world commands you to tell him, you miserable sinner! For fire-stealer and crony of mortals though you may be, one thing is sure: you can see into the future more clearly and more true than all the other gods together."

"You come swaggering here to play the bully," retorted Prometheus, "but can't you see that such airs do not suit a servant? If you want to learn something, I'll tell you just this, and straight out: when Zeus is overthrown, all his slaves and hangers-on will fall with him! Who are you to call me a thief, when you've been one from the cradle! And can fire be stolen, let alone a spark? You stand there as if you didn't know that Zeus still has all the fire he wants, since he has a whole handful of thunderbolts to himself. Take your orders back to your master and return where you came from this very instant!"

"Come on, now, enough of that," replied Hermes. "Tell me the secret. No one flouts the will of Zeus as rashly as this.

Besides, why should I pay for your stubbornness?"

"What I had to say, I've said. Now get out of my sight!"

"You always were a loud-mouthed fellow", replied Hermes, "and you'll pay for your insolence!"

"If you think I'd exchange my sufferings for your servile post, then you're mistaken," responded the titan. A thousand times better to be the slave of this rock than to sink to being Zeus' most faithful servant."

"I see you hate me as much as you hate him."

"I hate all those whom I helped and who did me ill in return."

"Is that why you resist the will of the lord of the world?"

"The only thing I resist is injustice."

"What is just and what is unjust, only he who rules over gods and men can decide."

"No!" roared Prometheus. "That I will never accept. We cannot make justice out of injustice or turn right into wrong simply because it suits us. What did men do to Zeus to deserve such harsh treatment at his hands? Why did he take the fire back? Why did he want them to starve as before? Why did he drown them in the flood? Can you tell me?"

"I can only tell you one thing," replied Hermes. "He is our father and the mightiest of the gods, and the greatest sin of all is to go against his wishes."

"No, injustice is the greatest sin, if you want to know the truth. Only love can create beauty, not hatred. Or perhaps you'd prefer to see the earth savage and desolate. Look at the green meadows and the flocks grazing peacefully in them. Look at the men working their fields. Look at the villages. Look at the cities with their temples and their statues. Look at the altars and the sacrifices whose sweet smoke rises to the sky – thanks to the fire which you say I "stole". See how they praise and worship you on Olympus, but never me. Oh, no! My name may never be spoken. And why? Because I gave help to mortals, and not a little to immortals, too. And this is the payment I received for my efforts! But I tell you: injustice shall not rule for ever, and though I am now being punished unfairly, the time will come when Zeus will receive the punishment he truly deserves!"

"Enough of your threats. Just do your duty and tell me what you owe: how can Zeus be saved?"

"If I owed Zeus his salvation I would give it him," the titan answered. "But he owes me mine. And there is another thing he must do, and that is give justice to mortals – not let violence rule and justice languish in chains!"

"Prometheus, there is one thing you must understand: Zeus cannot be changed. And if you do not speak, more's the pity for you."

"I cannot be changed either – and more's the pity for Zeus!"

"Fool!" cried Hermes. "Come down to earth and see reason!"

"It seems I've come down quite far enough, since I've sunk

to talking with servants!"

"How dare you speak to me like that! Do you take me for a stable boy?"

"Boy, you say? You're even more brainless than a baby if you think you can wrest my secret from me. I will not tell Zeus how he may be saved until he frees me from these bonds and shows that he will rule the world with love. Even if he subjects me to the vilest tortures his twisted mind can dream up, he will not break my spirit and force me to reveal who will cast him from his throne."

"Do you really think you have anything to gain by behaving like this?" Hermes demanded.

"You're the patron of merchants," Prometheus sneered, "and you speak like one yourself. I never considered my own profit. Only one thing concerns me: that justice should be counted and not injustice!"

"You're a rebel and you speak like one. You do not accept the rule of Zeus. But now hear what he has decided for you, and then keep your secret to yourself if you dare – for compared with what lies in store for you, your present sufferings will seem a mere game. A peal of thunder and a shaft of lightning will split asunder the rock to which you are pinned. At the same moment the earth will open wide and you will be swallowed in the inky depths of Tartarus, rock and all. And when long ages have passed, you will emerge into the light once more to face your greatest trial. An eagle will come each

day, tear your body open with its talons and devour your liver.
In the night your wound will heal over, but the next day the
bird will return and rip your flesh open once more. This will
go on and on for ever, and your sufferings shall have no end.
Now think carefully, for you know that Zeus is not bluffing.
His thunderbolt is poised to strike. The time has come for
you to show more wisdom and less daring, if you want my
advice."

By the time Hermes had finished, the eyes of the Oceanides
were flooded with tears. The sky had filled with black clouds.
The Oceanides looked around fearfully. So more frightful
tortures were possible, after all! Finally they went down on
their knees before Prometheus and begged him to follow
Hermes' advice and bow to his master's will.

"It is no shame to change one's opinion," the Oceanides
urged. "What is shameful is for a wise man to be stubborn
when he knows he is in the wrong."

"Hermes has taught me nothing I did not know already,"
retorted Prometheus as if he had not heard. "I have known for
years of all the tortures that await me." Then he shouted in a
mighty voice. "Get on with it, then! Let the thunder and lightning of Zeus fall on me and shake the earth to its very foundations. Let the wind lash the waves into fury and the raging
hurricane wreak havoc upon all creation. Let the sun and the
stars change their course in the heavens and let my body be
thrown into inky Tartarus. But be sure of one thing: my reso-

lution will not waver!"

"Strange indeed," mused Hermes. "Such an answer I never expected to hear." Then, lifting his head, he shouted, "Is your mind so unhinged that it can no longer tell you where your interest lies? And as for you, o daughters of Oceanus, who feel such sympathy for him, I tell you for your own good: beware! Leave this place now, as quickly as you can, for the mere sound of one of Zeus' thunderclaps will be enough to drive you out of your minds!"

"Have you any other words of comfort for us?" replied the Oceanides bitterly. "No, of course not. But don't trouble yourself on our account. We have learned to hate the sight of traitors!"

The dire consequences which Hermes had threatened were not long in making themselves felt. The sky darkened and the whole of creation reechoed with rolling peals of thunder. Lightning split the heavens like fiery snakes. The winds spun together in a great column through which Zeus hurled a fearsome thunderbolt that shot the resolute titan into the air upon his rock. At the same moment the earth split in two and the rock-bound Prometheus was cast headlong into the pitch-black depths of Tartarus.

With cries of fear and despair, the Oceanides fled from the scene, while Hermes peered down from the safety of a high rock. He was frightened yet thoughtful. Although he hated Prometheus, he could not hide his admiration for him.

*...The rock-bound Prometheus was cast headlong into
the pitch-black depths of Tartarus...*

"Truly, such a god should not suffer a fate like this," he murmured to himself. "Now to be thrown into the bottomless depths of Tartarus, and tomorrow to be exposed on the peaks of the Caucasus once more to have his flesh torn every day by Zeus' eagle. And to think that this horrible torture will never end, for even if anybody should someday wish to save him it can never be done, since there is no one who can break the heaven-forged chains which hold him bound."

As these thoughts passed through Hermes' mind he little guessed that in time a hero named Heracles would be born, and that he would smash the fearless titan's unbreakable chains.

For countless years Prometheus lay buried in the depths of the earth, alone in the thick darkness of Tartarus. Still bound and nailed to his rock, he could not find a moment's rest from his sufferings, not an hour's sleep to bring him sweet oblivion.

And when the time came for him to be brought up into the light of day once more, a terrible earthquake tumbled the depths of Hades together, the rock was hurled far into the air and then, with a great peal of thunder, rammed back into the high peaks of the Caucasus, where it had stood before.

Blinded by the glaring light, the torture-wearied titan could see nothing at first. But when he was at last able to open his eyes, he saw before him the savage and threatening form of Zeus' slave, Violence.

The fellow wasted no time on preliminaries.

"Out with it," he snarled. "Come on! Tell me the secret which will save the ruler of the world. For now that you have seen the greatness of Zeus' power you must have realised that you can no longer oppose his will."

But Prometheus remained silent. The mere sight of Violence filled him with loathing, and he turned away his head.

"I have spoken!" roared Violence. "And I demand an answer from you!"

"Ah, how I would prefer not to have this slave standing in front of me," thought Prometheus. "A thousand times better for the eagle to begin tearing me at once than to have this creature troubling my mind."

"Listen, Prometheus," Violence went on. "If you do not obey, Zeus' eagle will be here in an instant. Your salvation lies in your own hands."

"If Zeus needs helpers like you," growled the fearless titan, "then I'm better off nailed to this rock. Let his bird of prey come and tear at my vitals. I shall not give in! And now, get out of my sight, you worm!"

The unexpected wrath of Prometheus' reply scared the wits out of Violence, who immediately fled back to Olympus.

But then the eagle hove into sight, a huge bird of prey with hooked beak and curved talons. Swooping like lightning upon the chained titan it began its foul work. As it ripped open his flesh and tore at his liver, Prometheus gritted his teeth with pain, but bore the terrible assault without a murmur. Even when the eagle had flown away, the gaping wound in Prometheus' side tortured him all day. Only in the evening did the gash heal over and his liver grow again – not so that the titan's pains would be eased for ever, but only that the hideous suffering might be renewed the following day. Year after year this went on, for entire centuries, and all the while the great benefactor of mankind hung there in chains, nailed upright to the rock, suffering, hoping and waiting.

The daughters of white-haired Oceanus often came to ease his pain. Their admiration for Prometheus grew till it knew no bounds. They marvelled at his endurance and said,

"Ah, how can you stand this endless torment, fearless titan, when we cannot even bear to look upon it?"

And true to their word, as soon as the Oceanides heard the ominous wing-beats of the eagle they would run to hide with cries of despair.

The years rolled by, but the daughters of old Oceanus did not forget Prometheus and never neglected to keep him company in his suffering. They often spoke to him of men: of their troubles and of their hopes, their sorrows and their joys.

The chained titan listened to the Oceanides with attention, but it made his heart bleed to think that he could no longer help.

However, the sea-maidens had some comfort to offer him.

"Little by little, men are making progress, Prometheus. They are acquiring skill in the arts you taught them and mak-

...Year after year this went on, for entire centuries...

ing good use of the fire which was your gift. Their life is improving."

And as time went by, they had ever happier news for him.

"Time cures many ills, Prometheus," they told him. "A lot of things have changed on earth, but on Olympus, too. With the passing of time, Zeus has come to love the new generation of men. The gods call them "the race of heroes". Led by Athena, but aided by Demeter and Hephaestus and others, the immortals give mankind their help. They give praise to the gods in return, and Zeus is pleased. The gods often live with men. They eat and drink with them, share in their joys and weep with them over the harsh blows of fate. In war they are at man's side, and in times of peace they are never far away. The gods often fall in love with mortals and thus are born the demi-gods, who become rulers and mighty heroes who add new lustre to the human race."

When they had spoken these words, the Oceanides looked Prometheus full in the eyes. And for the first time since he had been chained to the rock, they saw the unflinching titan's face light up.

"I feel no hatred towards Zeus," he said. "There is but one thing I have always wanted: to help men and not make their lives a misery. And I rejoice that he who wished to make me his enemy because I helped mortals has now become a friend of mankind himself."

"Wisely spoken, unhappy titan," the Oceanides replied.

"The frightful tortures that have flayed your body down the centuries have not embittered your mind. Your thoughts have remained pure and your feelings as noble as they always were."

"Listen, oh daughters of my greatest friend," replied Prometheus. "Blind, barren stubbornness is logic's greatest enemy. Even the most unbending spirit will bow before kind-heartedness. Zeus did me a great evil, just as he did to mankind; but if he has now decided to treat them well, I shall not be the one to harbour hatred for him. Indeed, the time has now come when I may tell Zeus the secret which will save him."

"Your wise decision has given us joy and new courage," said the Oceanides, and our growing hope is strengthened by the kindness and wisdom of your words. And now something seems to tell us that an end to your frightful sufferings will not be long in coming. We feel sure of it. The hour is drawing near when the great Heracles will appear to smash your unbreakable bonds." .

"You are not mistaken," answered Prometheus. "I feel it in the air. Yes, Heracles is near at hand, the hero I have waited for all these centuries."

When they heard these words, the Oceanides could not contain their joy. They embraced one another, danced and gambolled, then ran and climbed the neighbouring rocks and began to call,

"Heracles! Heracles! Heracles!"

And indeed, before very long, a human figure appeared, silhouetted on a distant peak.

"Heracles!" the Oceanides shouted again, all together.

"I am coming!" came the hero's voice faintly, from far away.

It was a scene of indescribable joy. The Oceanides kissed and embraced one another. Some ran towards the approaching hero and others to Prometheus to tell him the happy news.

Heracles did not know why they were calling him, but he realised that they wanted help, and so he wasted no time. With giant steps he bounded over the jagged rocks, up hills and down valleys, but moving ever forwards.

Heracles was always ready to give help to those in trouble. He had dedicated his whole life to that purpose. That is why he did not hesitate to enter into the service of Eurystheus, the jealous and cowardly king of Mycenae who thought that he could humiliate the hero, or even put him out of the way for ever, by sending him off to accomplish twelve seemingly impossible labours. But all the tasks were completed, and many others besides, because Heracles realised that in achieving them he was helping mankind. He rid the world of dangerous beasts. He fought against evil-doers. He defeated savage warriors. He opened new roads into distant regions. He joined the sea to the boundless ocean. He lifted the whole earthly globe upon his shoulders. He wrestled with Charon and defeated him. He fought against the Giants. He voyaged with the sun in his golden boat. He ranged over the whole world, from North to South and from East to West. He even descended into Hades and returned by the same route, that road which no man ever journeys back upon.

And now he found himself in the Caucasus, because the time had come for him to accomplish his most challenging and noble feat: to free the great friend of mankind from his long imprisonment.

At last Heracles stood facing Prometheus from the top of a nearby rock. For days now he had been wandering among the mountains. He had been among the heroes who had joined the Argonauts on their expedition, but had got lost in the forest at one of the Argo's anchoring-places. Now, however, as he faced the chained and nail-pierced titan upon the rockface opposite, he realised why he had been fated to lose his way, and why his steps had led him straight to this wild and deserted spot where he now beheld Prometheus suffering the most hideous tortures that the mind of god or mortal could conceive.

Heracles was overcome with pity for the unjustly punished titan. But he was determined that his horrible suffering should not continue for much longer. Jumping down from the rock he stood upon, he ran to help. When he reached Prometheus, he could find no words to express his pity and admiration for the unflinching titan.

Suddenly, a hideous screeching filled the air. The Oceanides

covered their faces in alarm. Heracles looked up into the sky
and saw the eagle soaring on high. It was the hour when the
vile bird of prey always came to tear at the titan's vitals.
Heracles did not waste a moment. He took an arrow from the
sheath that hung from his shoulder, bent his bow with all his
mighty strength and took aim. There was a great twang as the
bow-string was released, and the arrow shot up into the air
with a loud whistle. In a moment the eagle was tumbling from
the heights, its wings fluttering uselessly as its heavy body
dragged it down. It plummeted into the foaming sea which
sucked it down into its dark depths in the twinkling of an eye.

The Oceanides let out cries of joy when they saw the eagle's fall.

At that very moment winged Hermes swooped from the
sky on a mission from Zeus. Prometheus knew what the swift-
footed god had come for and he told him,

"There is no need to plead with me this time. The moment
has come for Zeus to learn the great secret. But as you see,
the time has also come for me to be set free. Here is Heracles,
the hero I have waited for these endless years. None but he
can smash these unbreakable chains. No one, I say, neither
god nor mortal."

Yet Hermes still had one more question to put.

"But was it not Zeus' command that you should remain
pinned to this rock for all eternity? Much as I pity you, how
can Zeus' decision be revoked? We all know that such a thing

is not possible, even if the lord of the world himself were to wish it."

"Do not puzzle your mind with such questions," Prometheus replied. "A way will be found to free me without flouting the will of Zeus. Now listen carefully to the great secret I shall reveal, and take word back to your master: he must not marry Thetis, daughter of the great sea-wizard Nereus. For the Fates have written that Thetis shall give birth to a son who will be mightier than his father. And it is this son who will cast him from his throne!"

Hardly had these words left Prometheus' mouth than Hermes was speeding back to Olympus with the warning.

As soon as he had left, Heracles stepped forward and said, "At last! Now I can do what I want. Nobody told me that the great friend of mankind must remain here for ever."

And with these words the mighty hero lifted his great club and began to strike at the chains with such force that the whole rock began to shake. It was a hard task, for the heaven-forged links resisted even such superhuman blows, but Heracles' determination to release the unjustly-punished titan was so great that his strength grew as he struck. Each blow was twice as strong as the one before. Blinding sparks flew up in ever brightening cascades as he attacked the chains. Showers of thunderbolts seemed to be falling around the hero. All nature shook and the whole wide waste of the Caucasus echoed and re-echoed to the herculean blows. It was not long before the "unbreakable" chains were smashed to pieces. As soon as the links had fallen apart, the mighty hero tugged the nail out of Prometheus' chest. The titan took a deep breath of fresh air and fell, free at last, into Heracles' sturdy arms. The two men clasped each other in silent joy, while the Oceanides wept out of sheer happiness.

"I cannot find words to thank you, mighty hero," said Prometheus at last. "You have given me my freedom, and nothing I could say would ever express my gratitude."

"I have never learned to accept gratitude," replied Heracles. "And nothing could give me more happiness than to have been chosen to give man's greatest friend his freedom. People call me a hero, and perhaps they are right. I have accomplished many difficult tasks and it may well be that I shall be remembered for them for ever. But this has been the hardest feat of all. For those chains were truly unbreakable. Yet of one thing I am sure: not this, nor all my achievements put together can ever be compared with yours. For what you have done required a strength of body and will a thousand times greater than my own – a strength such as no other being has ever possessed."

"Listen to my words, Heracles, and let the whole world mark them", replied Prometheus. "All of us, even the humblest of mortals, can find the strength that is required when we set our faces against injustice – for the greater the injustice that reigns in this world, the greater the strength we find

...The whole wide waste of the Caucasus echoed and re-echoed to the herculean blows...

to fight it." With these words Prometheus fell silent. The time
had come for him to rest at last.

And thus the most frightful ordeal the world has ever known
came finally to an end. Zeus and Prometheus were reconciled
and peace was re-established amongst the gods.

In obedience to the titan's prophecy Zeus did not take Thetis
for his wife. Although the lovely Nereid was immortal, the
Olympians gave her in wedlock to a mortal man, Peleus, king
of Phthia. And as Prometheus had foretold, she gave birth to
a son who was far mightier than his father. His name was
Achilles, the greatest war-lord of all Greece.

Only for Hermes was there still a nagging doubt. "How is
it that Zeus' decision was not upheld?" he asked himself. But
not for long, for even that question was soon answered.

Zeus commanded Hephaestus to fashion a ring, and to set
in it a stone from the rock where Prometheus had hung in
chains. The lord of the world offered it as a gift to the indomi-
table titan and he wore it ever afterwards to show his gratitude for the gesture. And thus it came about that the will of
Zeus was respected to the last. "Let Prometheus be bound to
the rock for all eternity" Zeus had said – and bound he was!

THE MOON, THE DAWN
AND THE SUN

Just as in our days, when the sun rises each morning, lights the earth and then sets, or when the moon makes its slow way across the sky each night, so it was in those distant times when mighty Zeus reigned on Olympus, or when gods and men were ruled by the fearsome Cronus, or even further back in time, when the god Uranus was the first master of the world. For this is how things have always been upon our earth and it is how they will always be.

The only difference is that in those far off days, men embroidered these daily occurrences with their vivid imagination. They gave human shapes to the Moon, the Dawn, and the Sun and saw them as fair and mighty gods.

They were brothers and sisters, they said. Their father was the titan Hyperion and their mother the titaness Theia.

The moon goddess, Selene, they imagined as clothed in a long, white dress, appearing each night in a chariot drawn by curly-horned bulls. In the quiet of the night she would sail slowly across the sky, among the clouds, and shine her peaceful, silvery light down on the earth.

But on Selene's pure and lovely face were the shadows of a great sorrow. The goddess mourned eternally for her beloved Endymion, who could neither speak nor answer her call but lay in a sleep from which he could never be woken.

Endymion, who was as fair as the immortal gods, had begged the mighty Zeus that he might fall into this everlasting sleep so that he would never grow old, and the lord of the world had commanded Hypnos, god of sleep, to grant him his wish.

Now he slept forever, yet Selene did not cease to love him for this reason. Every night she came to caress his face with her silver fingers and to whisper tender, pain-filled words in his ear. For she knew that her beloved would never open his eyes again, nor ever awake to tell her that he loved her. This is why Selene is always sad and pale.

Selene's sister was the goddess of the dawn, rosy-fingered Eos. The children of Eos and Astreus are the stars which deck the sky at night and the gods of the four winds.

When night was drawing to its close, Eos would spring into the sky to announce to the world the approach of her brother the Sun, the bright god Helios. Clothed in a robe of yellow gossamer, she rose into the heavens gently fluttering her white wings. With a faint and gentle light which spread over all things and grew ever stronger, Eos slowly dissolved the darkness of the night. In her left hand she held a golden vessel filled with cool water. She would dip her fingers into it and then scatter shining pearls of dew upon the earth, the meadows and the flowers.

Before long she would reach the East and the golden palace of Helios, god of the sun. Then rosy-fingered Eos would open wide its tall gates and out would come the great god of day, standing on his golden chariot, drawn by four winged horses. A few moments passed and then the chariot rose from the ground and Helios appeared over the horizon, radiant and majestic, to set out on his daily journey.

It was a hard task the shining god had to carry out each day. He had to drive his chariot high into the sky without straying an inch from his course. On his way he would encounter monsters and fearful beasts such as the Scorpion, the Crab and the Lion. But these held no fears for him and he steadily followed the tracks his chariot wheels had worn in their daily journey across the heavens. No beast had ever dared stand in the great god's path or frighten his horses, for they all knew that if they did so they would be burned by his flames. And so the god continued on his way unafraid and happy in his daily task, knowing that as he went he spread light around him, warmed the earth and gave life to all its creatures.

Day drew towards its close. The chariot of Helios sank lower and lower. Now the god guided his horses with even greater skill, holding the reins firmly lest they lose their footing and his shining chariot tumble earthwards – for that would mean the end of the world.

As evening approached, Helios set in slow majesty. Bathed in a thousand colours, the whole of nature praised the great god for his lovely and noble work, while countless voices seemed to say:

"O gods, let us live to see again the bright light of the sun!"

The sun set. Helios sank into the west, far away upon the boundless ocean, near the Fortunate Isles, in the furthest reaches of the world. There a golden boat awaited to carry him swiftly on the ocean's currents back to his shining palaces in the East.

These palaces were the work of Hephaestus, who had wrought them from gold and silver and precious stones and blended them so skilfully that they shone with all the colours of the rainbow.

In these gleaming halls, which the great craftsman of

Olympus had built for him, the shining god would rest for the night. And when day was near a cockerel would crow, its green wings shot with gold, to waken the god of the day. Mighty Helios would rise at once and prepare himself for his long and difficult journey. Thus every day, for thousands of years, the tireless god rode his shining chariot across the skies, spreading light, warmth and kindliness over the earth.

Helios always made a smooth journey, holding precisely to the same path and never straying off course. On one occasion, however, this orderly rhythm was disturbed, and the sun showed its terrible power. The forests blazed, the flames spread and whole towns were burned to the ground.

How could such a disaster have occurred?

The answer to that is given to us in the myth of Phaethon, son of Helios.

Phaethon, a handsome and bold young man, lived on earth with his mother, Clymene. He very much admired his father and his great works and was forever seeking an opportunity to cross the heavens in the golden chariot of the Sun.

One day, he was insulted by Epaphus, the son of Zeus by the princess Io of Argos. Now Epaphus was extremely proud of the blood that flowed in his veins, and to make Phaethon feel small he told him:

"Your mother is lying when she tells you Helios is your father, and what is worse, you will never be able to find out which mortal's son you really are."

Clymene's young son was deeply offended by this insult.

"An arrow in the heart would be better than the words I have just heard," groaned Phaethon, and he immediately ran to his mother to tell of the mocking words Epaphus had cast in his face.

"I would never have been ashamed to be the son of a mortal father," he told her, "but what does fill me with shame is the thought that I have been deceived by my own mother!"

"What are you saying, my son?" cried Clymene. "Do you think I could ever have deceived you? Go to your father's palace this very night, and let Helios himself put your mind at rest."

Phaethon ran to the golden halls of the shining god, and as soon as he saw his father he cried:

"O bright Helios, I have always called you father until now, but I do not know if I should call you by that name any longer." And then he told the sun god of the suspicion that was gnawing at his mind.

"Who told you such a thing? I shall burn him up this very instant and show the world that no one may insult my son!"

"I do not want you to burn him with your fire, father, but give me some proof which will force the haughty Epaphus to hold his tongue forever."

"Ha! Ha!" laughed Helios, "So Epaphus is up to his little tricks again! But is it worth getting so upset over one of his silly jokes?"

"It was no joke, father. He was speaking seriously. I can't look him in the eyes again. I would rather disappear from the face of the earth than be jeered at and told that I will never be able to find out whose son I am."

"Shout it from the mountain-tops: you are my son and your mother is Clymene!"

"Yes, but who will believe me?"

"Then what can I do to help you, my son?" asked Helios affectionately.

"First, I want you to swear that you will do me whatever favour I ask of you."

"It seems a small enough matter for me to give you my solemn oath upon. But since you seem so distressed, I will do so to make you happy. There! I swear by the holy waters of the Styx that I will do whatever you ask of me."

And then the daring young man cried:

"I want to ride your chariot across the skies, just for one day."

"Ah, what are you asking, my son? Not even Zeus himself, the mightiest of all the gods, can drive this chariot. Ask anything else of me you wish, but do not ask me for your own destruction."

"I have no wish to destroy myself. I simply wish to fly, and you promised that you would let me."

"Yes, I gave you my word, and were it only given lightly I

could not go back on it. How much less could I break an oath sworn on the holy waters of the Styx! But that is not what I am trying to tell you. Ask me for something else. There are thousands of favours you could beg of me, and yet you have to go and choose the very one which will bring destruction upon you."

"There is nothing else I want. If I really am your son, give me your chariot so that I may fly high in the sky, become the sun and light the world, if only for one day – and then nobody will ever dare insult me again."

"You are bold and fearless, my son, but you are still a child and you will lose your life in the attempt. That would be a tragedy. I tell you again: it is not too late to change your mind. Those horses are headstrong, don't you understand? You will be frightened by terrible monsters, veer from your path, and that will be the end."

But Phaethon fell sobbing into his father's arms and begged him to give way. And Helios, who had given his solemn word, realized that there was no other choice for him but to put into his son's hands the means of his own destruction.

Although he did not really believe that there was any way of saving him, Helios took a magic ointment and smeared it on the young man's body so he would not be burned by the flames. And then he said in a despairing voice:

"Hold the reins firmly, my son, so that the horses do not realize that they are in the hands of an inexperienced driver.

Do not use the whip on them at all, in case they turn savage. Keep to the wheel-tracks you see in the sky. As you go up, be careful not to stray from your path and get lost. When you reach the heights, do not look down, in case you feel dizzy. And on the downward path, draw the reins in hard, lest the chariot topple over and be smashed to pieces on the earth below. But what is the point of my telling you all this? Let me drive the chariot. The time has come when we must light up the earth. Here comes Eos to open the gates."

But before he could do anything, Phaethon had jumped into the chariot, seized the reins and given them a violent tug. He bid a hasty farewell to his father as the horses opened their white wings and cantered lightfooted out of the great gates of the sun god's palace.

"Where are you going, my son?" cried Helios, dashing after him. "Phaethon, turn back! You will kill yourself! Ah, rash youth! How the unknown draws you, the broad vault of the sky, the light of the sun! Alas, how unjust that such daring should be tumbled into the dark depths of Hades! Phaethon! Do you not hear me? Come back!"

But the young man was no longer listening. The horses had started to climb into the sky and his joy was beyond description. Epaphos would never dare to insult him again.

Not that such details worried him any longer, for nobler thoughts occupied his mind as his shining chariot left the earth and the golden rays of the sun gave light, life and warmth to the world. It is truly a great thing to be able to do good, thought Phaethon. Ah, if only I could drive this chariot more often!

Carried away by such thoughts, Phaethon forgot where he was. The horses sensed that they were no longer under firm control, and that the chariot felt lighter. Their forelegs reared up, they left the path and bolted. It was only when Phaethon lost sight of the chariot tracks that he realized what danger threatened him. He tried to bring the chariot back on course, but the horses would not obey him and galloped towards the unknown.

Suddenly a huge scorpion loomed in the sky ahead. Horror-stricken, Phaethon let go of the reins, and that was the beginning of the end. Completely unchecked now, the horses ran wherever they wanted. Sometimes they charged downwards and then the earth caught fire, sometimes they galloped high into the skies again, and then the heavens burst into flames. Phaethon choked as he breathed in the burning air. Now there was nothing he could do. He knew neither where he was going nor how to control the horses. He bitterly regretted that he had not listened to his father's advice, but it was far, far too late, for by now the whole of nature was a hellish sea of fire. The earth below him burned, wrapping twin-peaked Parnassus in its flames. Mount Ida and shady Pelion were set ablaze. Wooded Helicon and lofty Taygetos were bathed in a reddish glow, while the Caucasus and all the forests of Asia were set on fire. Entire cities and nations were

...The horses sensed that they were no longer under firm control...

wiped out. Wells and streams dried up and the nymphs ran to hide in the deepest caves. Even the mighty Nile and the Euphrates boiled, and clouds of steam rose from the sea. The earth dried up and was split by cracks so deep that the fiery rays of the sun penetrated into the darkest regions of Hades.

Then the great goddess Earth, the mother of all things, rose up and cried to Olympus in ringing tones:

"O lord Zeus, ruler of the world, can you not see that the whole earth is wrapped in flames? Must I, too, be lost, along with the rivers and the shady woods? Must all the races of mankind that feed upon my soil be destroyed along with every other living creature on this planet? Must old chaos reign again, and all that has been achieved become mere ashes? Must earth and sky, gods and men, life and love be brought to nothing? O Zeus, save the earth from these flames at once, or else it will be too late."

Suddenly, from behind a cloud, the great figure of Zeus rose up and, drawing back his right arm, loosed a thunderbolt which in an instant quenched every flame upon the earth. Then he launched another which struck Phaethon's chariot and smashed it into splinters. The son of Helios was hurled into space like a shooting star, his hair streaming fire, and fell into the river Iridanus, in the farthest reaches of the world.

The nymphs of the West, the Hesperides, ran to pick up his body which they buried tearfully on the river bank.

The next day, bright Helios did not appear in the sky. He

was weeping for his son, Phaethon, who had wanted to fly high and was destroyed because he would not believe that he lacked the strength to do so. But in his heart, the great god was proud – for though Phaethon was dead, his memory would remain for ever in the hearts of men. Helios knew that it is thanks to the bold and the fearless that the world moves forward.

But Phaethon's mother was inconsolable. She searched frantically for her son's body as though she had lost her mind. At last she found his grave by the Iridanus and wept in despair over the son who had thrown away his life.

Her daughters, the Heliades, stood at her side and mourned their brother with bitter tears. They could not bear to leave Phaethon all alone, so they stayed there by his grave, day after day, night after night, crying endlessly until the gods took pity on them and turned them into willow-trees. They took root there, their branches hanging sadly over the banks of the river Iridanus to let their tears drop into its waters. And ever since, such trees have been called weeping willows.

Thus ends the tale of Phaethon, the bold youth who died because he would not listen to his father's advice.

Now if you ever happen to read this myth again elsewhere, it may say that Phaethon's mother was not Clymene but Rhode. Do not be surprised by this, for all myths differ to a greater or lesser extent from place to place.

Rhode was a nymph whom Helios met and fell in love

with on the island that takes its name from her – the island of Rhodos. They had a number of children together, one of whom, so some people say, was Phaethon.

On that island, Helios was worshipped above all other gods. A marble temple was built for him in the island's capital, and every five years a great festival was held in his honour with athletics competitions, chariot races and artistic events. The famous Colossus of Rhodes, the largest statue ever built in Greece, was meant to represent Helios. It was erected at the entrance to the harbour, and was so big that ships could pass under its open legs. Built by Haris of Lindos, it was one of the seven wonders of the world.

In other words, Rhodes was an island dedicated to Helios, the great god of the day. Yet it came to be his in rather a curious fashion.

When the other gods shared out the world among themselves, Helios was away, and they forgot to give him his portion.

But the god whose task is to warm the hearts of men did not feel bitter about their forgetfulness.

"It does not matter," he said gently. "Today, when I was half way across the sky, I saw a new island rising from the sea. Give me that and I shall be more than satisfied."

Naturally enough, the other gods were only too happy to let him have it, for otherwise it would have meant sharing everything out again from the beginning.

And of course, the land Helios saw rising from the sea was the enchanting and sun-drenched island of Rhodes.

DIONYSUS
THE GOD OF GOOD CHEER

In those far off days when Zeus was the mighty ruler of the heavens and the earth, there was not a city in Greece where festivals and celebrations were not held in honour of the god Dionysus. While Athena, for example, was chiefly worshipped in the city of Athens, Apollo at Delphi, Poseidon at Corinth and so on, Dionysus was worshipped everywhere. Indeed, it was not long before his worship spread beyond the borders of Greece until it finally embraced almost the whole of the known world. And that is something which never happened with any other Greek god.

There was nothing strange or unnatural about the fact that the worship of Dionysus spread so far and wide. Men loved him immediately, for he was the god of good cheer, merry-making and wine, and the festivals in his honour were celebrations which sweetened men's lives.

Dionysus was the son of Zeus and Semele, daughter of Cadmus, founder of Thebes. He was born in a very strange way. Indeed, one could say that the god of wine was born twice, as we shall see immediately.

Semele was a princess of such loveliness that people said her beauty and her grace surpassed even that of the immortal goddesses of Olympus.

Zeus was stirred by the beauty of Cadmus' daughter, and, being the lord of gods and men, he had little difficulty in winning her affections.

Time went by and soon Semele was carrying Zeus' son Dionysus in her womb. However, the tender feelings of motherhood-to-be were not destined to bring her the joy they brought to ordinary mortals.

The goddess Hera, wife of Zeus, was bitterly jealous of the lovely Semele and to take revenge she appeared before her and said:

"Zeus has never loved you, and if you don't believe me, ask him to appear before you in all his godly majesty and just see how he refuses you the favour."

Not suspecting why Hera had made this suggestion to her, Semele asked the lord of the world to grant her any favour she desired. And when Zeus innocently agreed she told him:

"You never appear before me as a god, but always as a man. Handsome and splendid, yes, but still a man. I want to see you just once in all your Olympian majesty, standing before me in your real form, as the lord of the heavens and the earth, bathed in all the radiance of your glory."

"You foolish creature," Zeus replied. "No mortal has the strength to face such a sight. Ask me whatever other favour you wish, for the one you have chosen will destroy you."

With Zeus' answer, Semele's doubts became a certainty. "Hera was right," she said to herself, and then, with the courage of despair she cried:

"I want that or nothing! If you love me, you must grant me the favour I begged of you!"

And Zeus, having given his word, could no longer refuse. "Unhappy mortal!" he cried. "This is Zeus!"

At that moment, a blinding radiance filled the palace of Cadmus. The great lord of gods and men appeared before Semele, unbearably dazzling and magnificent, grasping a sheaf of thunderbolts which immediately shot from his hands and burned everything around him. The earth trembled and the palace rocked upon its foundations and tumbled into ruins among the flames.

Ringed by fire, Semele fell to the ground and, just before she died, gave birth to Dionysus.

Sadly, Zeus picked up the child, which had not even rested six months in its mother's womb, and, to save its life, tore open his thigh and sewed the infant up inside, to lie there until its right time should come. And so, three months later, the child was born again out of the thigh of Zeus.

Thus, although he had a mortal mother, Dionysus became immortal, for this second time he was born not of an earthly woman but of the mighty ruler of the world.

Zeus gave the young god to the Hyades, the kind-hearted nymphs of the woods, who tended him with loving care.

Later, to reward them for their pains, Zeus raised them up into the skies and placed them among the stars, where they became the constellation of the Hyades.

Dionysus grew up into a handsome, charming god, always gay and cheerful.

He was the first person in the world to plant vines and he worked hard to show men how to tend vineyards, make wine and gladden their lives with laughter, feasting, dance and song.

Dionysus did not live on Olympus, but wandered over the fields and forests of the earth. On his brow he wore a garland of vine leaves and in his hand he bore a rod wound in ivy with a pine cone at its tip.

The handsome god of joy was followed by a gay and noisy

band of satyrs and maenads.

These followers of his were a curious company. The satyrs were odd creatures. Some had horns and the hind legs of goats, while others had horses' tails. Many of them held the same ivy-covered rods as their master, while some beat cymbals arid others played flutes or sang. And they all danced wildly with the maenads, the frenzied nymphs of the woods. They were always followed by a donkey laden with flasks of wine from which the whole company drank toasts to one another.

Among them, one would often find Pan, the goat-footed god of the woods, and when he began to play his pipes, the whole noisy gathering would fall silent and approach, drawn by the magic power of his haunting music.

One person who struck a strange note in that happy, laughing throng was Dionysus' tutor, old Silenus, who followed them on his donkey, gloomy and silent. Although long past the age for dancing and merrymaking, he would not be parted from the lighthearted band, for he loved Dionysus greatly – and was more than a little fond of his wine, as well. Old Silenus knew that wine such as this was to be found nowhere else in the world, so he often joined in the fun and would sometimes take a flute and with a few, funny, lurching steps pretend to join in the happy company's dance.

Dionysus travelled all over the world with his companions, teaching men to cultivate the earth, to plant vines and to make wine, to sing and make merry.

Everywhere he went, the god of joy was received with open arms, altars were built in his name and he was honoured in dance and song.

There were a few, however, who would not recognize his worth and wished to fight against his influence. These people could not understand that it is impossible to stand in the way of joy and good humour and that sooner or later they will prevail.

The first mortal upon earth to cultivate grapes was the king of Aetolia, Oeneus. Dionysus had planted a few vines near the king's fields, and one day a herdsman of the king's, whose name was Staphylos, noticed that one of his goats was getting plumper every day. He followed her and found her eating some fruit which hung in bunches from a kind of bush he had never seen before. He tried some himself, found them delicious, and picked a few bunches to take to Oeneus. When the king saw how juicy they were, he squeezed them and made a drink. He had only taken a few sips when Dionysus appeared before him and asked what he thought of it.

"Superb!" said Oeneus and invited Dionysus to sit down at his table and be served. He then ordered his servants to set a rich banquet before the god, which they did, led by the eager Staphylos, who was anxious to see that the meal was perfect in every detail.

When they had eaten and drunk and were in a happy mood, the god of joy rose and said:

"You have honoured me. Now I shall honour you." Then, pointing to the fruit which Staphylos had gathered, he added:

"Let this fruit bear the name of the first mortal to discover it." And with these words he held up a bunch of grapes in his left hand. Then, raising an overflowing cup in his right hand, he went on:

"And let this drink bear the name of the mortal who first made it: Oeneus." For Oeneus, as you will have guessed, is really the same word as "wine" and "staphylos" is still the Greek name for a grape.

Then Dionysus revealed that it was he who had planted the bushes, so that he might teach them how to cultivate grapes and make the drink which filled men with gaiety and joy.

"And now, my friends, away with cares and sorrows!" cried Dionysus, lifting the cup to his lips and taking a sip of the wine. The others all followed suit, and then began a night of singing and dancing for everybody in the palace. From that time on, wine became the inseparable companion of all men's celebrations.

But wine does not only bring joy and good spirits. In Attica, indeed, the vine came not with songs and rejoicing, but misfortune and grief.

Once, when Dionysus was passing through Attica, he was welcomed by King Icarius, whose kingdom lay in the foot-hills of Mount Pentelicon, in the region which is even today called Dionysos after the god.

Icarius was so hospitable that in return Dionysus taught him how to plant vineyards and to make wine. He warned him, however, that he must keep it hidden and only give it to his guests in reasonable amounts.

Now either Icarius misunderstood the god, or he simply ignored his advice, for he left the wine where everybody could see it. And as a result, disaster struck the palace. For one day his shepherds uncorked the wineskins and drank so much that they became too drunk to know what they were doing. In their drunkenness they burst into the palace and after committing other acts of the most horrible violence, they killed Icarius himself. Then they dragged him out, heaved him into a well and dropped stones on him.

Now the unlucky king had a daughter named Erigone and she was led to the spot by her dog, Maera. A tree hung over the well where her father lay, and overwhelmed by his senseless murder she hanged herself from its branches. As for Maera, she howled night and day over the loss of her mistress until she, too, dropped dead beneath the tree where Erigone hung.

Filled with pity for the unfortunate trio, Dionysus and his father Zeus raised them to the skies and turned them into constellations, to save them from being carried off to the dark depths of Hades.

Ever since, men have remembered that wine does not only bring happiness and gaiety, but grief and misfortune. For this reason the Athenians took the myth of Icarius very seriously, as we shall see at the end of this story.

However, it was as a bringer of joy that the worship of Dionysus came to have such widespread and long-lasting influence, and thanks to it Dionysus became the first conqueror to bring the whole world under his power.

But let us hear of this victorious campaign from the lips of old Silenus, the young god's wise tutor.

During one of Dionysus' wild revels, Silenus wandered into a garden full of roses. Heavy with wine, he stretched out on the grass and fell into a deep sleep. As a result, his companions went on without him.

Now this garden belonged to Midas, king of Phrygia, and in the morning Silenus was found by the king's gardeners. Fearing that he might be a thief, they tied him up and took him to their master.

As soon as Midas set eyes on the old man he realized who he was and ordered them to set him free at once. And when the knots had been untied he invited Silenus to dine with him, to make him forget the indignity he had suffered at the hands of the gardeners.

By the time they had eaten and drunk, Silenus had quite regained his good spirits and began to tell Midas of the curious adventures that had befallen Dionysus and his band on their long campaign to give wine to the world.

"Can you imagine," he began, "that in Egypt we once fought a battle with Titans? That was after we had been all over Africa. We reached as far as Ethiopia and wherever we went we spread joy and good spirits. In Libya we met the warlike Amazons but they received us well and joined our band, and with their help we struck at the Titans, who had cast the god Ammon out of Egypt. We defeated them and Ammon became god of the Egyptians once more. This was

our first great victory, and others were to follow.

Later we went to Lydia, Persia and Arabia, and after that we headed north and reached as far as Bactria, a land in the depths of Asia watered by the rivers Oxus and Iaxartes.

We were welcomed everywhere we went. We offered the people wine and they danced and made merry with us. After that they were usually more than willing to be shown how to plant vines and to make wine for themselves. Only the hard-hearted king of Damascus fought against us – but insolence and impiety are never good weapons, and so we defeated his forces and Dionysus killed the king. Then all the people received us with songs and cries of joy.

But our expedition into India was the most difficult of all. We crossed the Euphrates on a rope bridge we made from thick creepers of vine and ivy.

The local people built a city there later and called it Zeugma, which means "the crossing-place" and now they show visitors pieces of the ropes we used to bridge the Euphrates.

When we reached the next great river in our path, the Tigris, we found a lion sent by mighty Zeus himself to carry us over to the other side.

At last we reached India, an unfriendly land where savage warriors lay in wait for us. At first they laughed and pointed when they saw our strange army. But when we beat them with our ivy-rods and our swords they soon began to respect our strength. Even so, we had to fight three years in India, they resisted us so stubbornly. In the end we attacked them with snakes and wild bulls which bellowed so hideously that they were seized with panic and took to their heels. We had defeated them but even so they were not completely subdued and continued to treat us as deadly enemies. We, on the other hand, treated them with unfailing kindness and so, little by little, we were able to teach them how to plant vines and cultivate the land and how to make wine from the heavy, luscious grapes. It was only when they had drunk the first of the wine that they finally buried their quarrel with us. Then their hatred turned to love and they built altars to Dionysus and held great feasts and festivals in his honour.

After that we left India and headed even further east. We reached a great river which ran out into a sea whose waters spun in a gigantic whirlpool. On the banks of the river stood tall trees with succulent red berries hanging from their branches. More unknown fruit hung gleaming from the trees on the opposite bank. We were reaching out to pluck the berries from the nearest trees when Dionysus suddenly shouted:

"Don't touch! Whoever eats one of those will be seized by horrible pains and die moaning in agony!"

We all drew back at these words, but soon our mouths were watering again at the sight of the fruit which glowed in the sun on the opposite bank.

"And nor can we eat of those," added Dionysus. "For whoever tastes those fruit becomes younger. No! Don't be so impatient to pick them. Don't look so happy! For next he becomes a youth again, then a child, then a baby, until finally he disappears altogether – and it makes no difference whether he's a mortal or a god. The signs all point to one thing: we have reached the end of the world, and there is no way we can go any further."

And so we returned the way we had come.

Another time we headed west. We taught the people to

cultivate the vine in Italy, Galatia and Iberia. We even went to the land of the Hesperides and offered wine to Atlas, the mighty titan who bears the dome of the skies on his shoulders. Then we crossed the ocean and reached an unknown continent completely separated from all the other land-masses of the world. It is not joined to Europe, Africa, or even Asia. Immediately we set eyes on this land we were struck by its natural beauty, but even more, we admired its people. They were as fair as gods and as tall as giants. They lived in noble cities, the like of which we had seen nowhere else on our travels. Still more wonderful was the way they had ordered their lives. Their laws were based on kindliness and fair play

and so they lived happy and peaceful lives in a community governed by mutual respect and brotherly love.

They enjoyed working, taught their children the meaning of goodness and beauty, cultivated the arts and the sciences, and delighted in music and dancing, painting, sculpture and poetry. In other words, theirs was a civilization that we here could never even dream of.

We asked them why they never visited our lands and they told us:

"Only once have we ever made such a voyage. We had heard that the loveliest and most civilised country in your regions was the land of the Hyperboreans, and so we decided to visit it. We built a vast fleet, large enough to hold more than ten million people, and we set out. But when we arrived there and looked around, and compared what they had with what we had ourselves, how they lived and how our own lives were, we were so disappointed that we swore we would never again go voyaging to other regions, so ugly did your own parts seem, and so evil your way of life."

When they told us these things we felt ashamed and thoughtful for the first time in our lives. We departed, without even leaving any wine, for we realized they were the first people we had met who had no need of it."

Such stories and many others like them poured in an endless flow from old Silenus' lips and Midas was so enthralled that he begged him to stay and tell him even more.

Now Silenus was a good-natured creature and so he stayed and told Midas stories for nine whole days. At last, on the tenth day, he decided that he must take his leave, and, to show his gratitude, the king himself led him back to Dionysus.

Dionysus was delighted to get his old tutor back after such a long absence and in his enthusiasm he told Midas:

"Ask me any favour you like, and you shall have it immediately!"

And without really thinking, the king replied:

"Mighty Dionysus, let everything I touch be turned at once to gold."

"I took you for a wiser man," replied the young god sadly,

"but it shall be as you ask." And with these words he took Silenus and went.

As soon as the god had left, Midas broke a branch from a fig tree and it turned into gold immediately. He picked up a stone from the ground, and that, too, lay in his hand with a bright gleam. He plucked an apple from a tree and straight away it shone like one of the golden apples of the Hesperides. He washed his hands and golden drops flew sparkling from his fingers.

By the time Midas reached his palace, he was floating in a sea of happiness. He immediately started touching the doors, the chairs and the tables, and in an instant they turned to gold. But when he sat down to eat and seized the bread with his hand, he suddenly understood why Dionysus had been saddened by the favour he had asked. Whatever he picked up to eat was transformed to gold. Even the wine stuck in his mouth in a solid lump. Now he realized his terrible mistake and cried out in despair:

"Mercy, great Dionysus! Take pity on me and forgive me for my greed! Take your gift back!"

At once, Dionysus appeared before him and said:

"Go and wash at the source of the river Pactolus, so you may be cleansed of the gift you begged of me and the shame you have brought upon yourself."

Midas ran to the spot where the Pactolus springs out of the ground and washed himself clean in its crystal waters. And as he rinsed the god's gift from his body, the waters of the river began to glitter with gold. There has been gold in the Pactolus ever since, and even today the river's name is used by the Greeks to signify whatever brings boundless wealth to a man.

Dionysus was a god with awesome powers, and things went very ill with those who did not realize it. This is what happened to the Tyrrhenian pirates who were foolish enough to mistake him for a mortal.

As we have said before, Dionysus was nearly always to be found in the company of his noisy followers, but once he wanted to walk alone on the sea-shore. After he had gone some distance, he sat down on a rock to catch his breath and looked out over the calm sea at a ship sailing on the open water.

But on that ship were those fearsome pirates from the Tyrrhenian Sea who had become the terror of every sailor in the Mediterranean.

It was not long before they caught sight of Dionysus on the shore, and the captain told the steersman to bring the ship in towards him.

The pirates had no idea that this handsome and strongly built youth was a god and they thought they could catch him and sell him as a slave.

And so, as soon as they reached shore, they jumped from the ship, hurled themselves upon Dionysus, overpowered him and took him back on board, where they immediately tied him to the mast.

But Dionysus just gazed at them calmly, with an enigmatic smile upon his lips as if he were secretly laughing at them. And when they saw how handsome and god-like he was, the robbers were overawed – so much so that one of them, the steersman, cried:

"Let this young man go immediately, for he may be no common man, but an immortal god. We should take care, lest he turn out to be mighty Zeus, the wielder of thunderbolts, or Apollo, whose deadly arrows never miss their target, or even Poseidon the earth-shaker, who will send any ship to the bottom whose captain scorns his power."

But the pirate chief cut him off rudely, saying:

"You must be out of your mind if you think we're going to free a strong and handsome youth like this just because you've lost your nerve. Why, look at him! We could sell him for a fortune in Cyprus or Egypt. Who knows, as likely as not he's from some great, aristocratic family and then we can ransom him for more gold than we've ever set eyes on."

And with these words, he gave orders to set sail for the open sea.

The pirates were delighted by his promise of riches, but they had not sailed far before they saw to their surprise that Dionysus had burst his bonds.

"Do you call those knots?" roared the captain. "Can't you

see how strong he is? That's why I tell you he'll fetch a fortune. Come on, now, tie him up again at once – and this time so he can't move an inch!"

The pirates set about tying him up ten times tighter, but hardly a moment had passed before they saw Dionysus stretch his muscles slightly and the ropes snapped once again.

Then the steersman jumped up and urged them to put him back on shore again as fast as they could, but the captain intervened with a howl of rage.

The pirates looked at him nervously as he roared:

"No, I say! This is one opportunity we're not going to throw away! Can't you see what a lucky wind is blowing, you cowards? Can't you see the gods themselves have sent him to make our fortunes for us? And you want to let him go! Come on, bind him with the anchor chains, and then we shall see if he can free himself again!"

It was not long, however, before even the chains lay broken on the deck. The pirates stared open-mouthed, but within seconds an even greater miracle had taken place. A grapevine sprouted, curled its way up the mast and put forth bunches of ripe grapes, and straight away sweet wine began to flow along the decks. The rigging became green with ivy. Garlands of flowers wreathed the whole ship, and the air was filled with fragrance.

Seized with panic, the pirates rushed to the steersman.

"Full speed for the shore!" they cried in one voice – but it

*...Do not be afraid. I have taken a liking to you. I am
Dionysus, son of Zeus, the god of joy and good cheer...*

was too late. For suddenly their calm young prisoner turned himself into a fearsome lion and let out a roar which froze them all with fear. Then he leapt upon their captain and tore him into pieces. The pirates jumped into the sea to save themselves from the horrible beast, but Dionysus turned them all into dolphins. The steersman alone was left on board, gazing at the lion in fear. Not only did the beast not harm him, however, but a moment later he changed back into a young man. Then he went up to the steersman and said to him with a smile:

"Do not be afraid. I have taken a liking to you. I am Dionysus, son of Zeus, the god of joy and good cheer."

As we have said before, great feasts were held in every place to honour the mighty god Dionysus. These feasts were called the Dionysia and they were usually occasions for dancing, drinking and merrymaking.

One festival of this kind was held in the mountains at night, by the light of torches, and only women took part. Two of the greatest of these were held on mounts Parnassus and Cythaeron.

But the greatest and the jolliest Dionysia of all were in Athens itself. Out of these Athenian revels was born the art of comedy, while an even more important creation that had its roots in the Dionysiac festivals was ancient tragedy.

This began as dithyrambs, hymns to Dionysus sung by a chorus of young men disguised as goat-footed satyrs. Because of their appearance, the young men were referred to as "tragoe" – the Greek word for goat.

Players re-enacted mythical scenes from the life of Dionysus – dramatic stories with a tragic ending. One of the first and best-loved myths to be acted at the Athens festival was that of Icarius, and during the performance these young goatmen appeared and sang their odes, or hymns to Dionysus. And so, from the two Greek words "tragoe" and "odae" was born the word "tragedy", a name which has been applied ever since to all theatrical works in which the heroes very often suffer a terrible but undeserved fate, as did Icarius and Erigone.

That is the origin of tragedy, an art form which in Greece attained the highest level of drama and poetic expression.

Indeed, the first theatre to be built of stone and marble was the theatre of Dionysus. It lies at the foot of the Acropolis, in Athens, and can still be seen today.

GOAT-FOOTED PAN

Now the time has come for us to tell of the last of all the gods, the poorest, the ugliest and the most despised, the god whose own mother refused to acknowledge him. He is the god of the herdsmen, goat-footed Pan.

He was the son of Hermes and the nymph Dryope. He was

born ugly beyond belief: hairy, with pointed ears and horns and hoofs like a goat. The moment she set eyes on him, his mother gave a cry of horror and fled from his sight.

But Hermes took pity on the child and took him to be one of Dionysus' merry band, knowing that there he would be loved. As soon as the company saw him, they burst out laughing at his strange appearance and funny antics. They were delighted with him and welcomed him with open arms.

Pan was a god of the mountains and his favourite region was Arcadia, where he was born. The protector of shepherds and hunters, he also enjoyed dancing and song, but above all he loved to play upon his pipes, and we shall see presently how he happened to make them.

Unfortunately, without wishing to, the goatfooted god brought out an uncontrollable terror in people, which we call panic from the name Pan. Poor Pan did not want to do ill, and in battle he always used to help those whose cause was just, by stirring up panic among their enemies.

And he certainly did not want to frighten Syrinx, the beautiful wood nymph who filled his heart with love as soon as he laid eyes on her. Nevertheless, as soon as Syrinx saw the odd looking god, she fled from him in panic. Pan immediately set off in pursuit and a chase began which had a very strange and unforeseeable ending. As fast as he ran, the nymph ran faster and he could not catch her up. Now unluckily for Syrinx, she found her way blocked by the swollen river Ladon, and to her horror she saw that Pan was fast approaching. In desperation, she begged the river-god to save her and just as Pan was reaching out his hand to seize her arm, Ladon transformed her into a reed.

Overcome with longing for the lovely maiden who had vanished before his very eyes, Pan looked down at the reed which was now all that he held in his hand. He did not want to throw it away, and as he listened to the wind whistling through its hollow stem, an idea came to him. He cut it into a number of small pieces each a little shorter than the next, and, starting with the longest, stuck them in a row with wax. And thus he created a new musical instrument: the syrinx, or "pan-pipes" as we call them today. When he put them to his lips he was charmed by their notes and kept them by him always.

Pan was a great musician. It is said that only Apollo excelled him. But Pan would never accept this and decided to challenge the golden-haired god.

The contest took place at the foot of Mount Tmolus, in Phrygia, where Midas was king. They both agreed that the god of the mountain should be appointed judge, but they invited Midas to come and listen as well.

Pan played first. The sweet melodies from his pipes floated across the mountainside and the shepherds listened spellbound to notes which spoke to their hearts. Even the birds stopped their warbling to listen to the pipes of Pan, so entrancingly did he play.

Next, Apollo took up his lyre. And as his fingers touched its chords the most wonderful music came pouring forth and filled the mountainsides and the high valleys with its majestic sounds. All nature listened in bewitched silence, for so entrancing were the notes of Apollo's lyre that even the trees held their breath, and not a leaf stirred on the whole mountain.

When the song had ended, Tmolos declared Apollo the winner without a moment's hesitation.

"No! Pan is the winner!" cried Midas, unasked.

Scarlet with rage, Apollo went up to the king, caught him by the ears and hissed:

"Who asked you to be the judge? What do these ears know of music?" And as he spoke, he pulled; and as he pulled, so Midas' ears grew longer and longer, until they were those of a donkey – the most unmusical beast on earth.

Saddened by his defeat, Pan gave the unfortunate king a look of sympathy, then turned and was lost to sight in the forest where he can still be heard playing his sweet melodies to the spellbound nymphs and nereids of the mountains and the springs.

THE MUSES AND THE GRACES

"In Athens, there was once a time when the statues outnumbered the inhabitants." With these words, a much-travelled author of ancient times tried to show how much fine arts like music, poetry, dancing, the theatre, painting and sculpture were loved in the Greece of long ago.

There was indeed such a time, a wonderful period when the people of that corner of the world called Greece believed themselves protected by the gods of Olympus – or, rather, a time when they believed themselves to be led by immortal artists.

For did not Athens itself choose as its protector the god-

dess Athena, she who is said to have first taught men the
meaning of beauty and harmony? And was it mere chance
that to Apollo, god of music, were dedicated the two most
holy places in Greece, Delos and Delphi? What of Hephaestus, tireless master-craftsman; Dionysus, father of ancient
drama, and his followers, who were all musicians, singers
and dancers? What of Pan, who made the hillsides and the
forest glades echo to the sweet strains of his reed pipes? Take
Hermes, even: as a new-born babe, his first thought was to
fashion a lyre; and when he played it, he bewitched Apollo
himself.

And to the ranks of these gods we must add the countless
wood-nymphs and nereids whose dancing and song made
every stream and sea shore of Greece re-echo with sweet
melody.

And as if these divine beings were not enough to express
the Greeks' love for the fine arts, there were also the Nine
Muses and the Three Graces – all daughters of mighty Zeus.

The Muses were the goddesses who gave the world music,
poetry, dance and drama, and with them they brought joy,
laughter and tender feelings to the earth. In their hearts there
was no place for sorrow, but only happiness and gaiety.

"Love only what is beautiful, scorn ugliness" was the nine
sisters' advice, and thus they inspired men to create works of
art.

The people of Mount Helicon said that Zeus' beloved

daughters often came to the wooded slopes of their mountain, where shepherds heard their songs mingled with the chattering of the brooks and the chirping of the birds.

Even more often, the nine sisters were to be found at Delphi at the side of Apollo, or Master of the Muses, as the great god of music was also called.

When the golden-haired god lifted up his lyre and his fingers brushed its strings, the Muses would at once begin their song. Then, beneath the shady plane trees of the Castalian spring, the wood-nymphs and the nereids would gather for the dance. And the Phaedrian rocks, which towered above the spring, would take up their lovely melodies and send them rebounding back and forth till all the slopes of Parnassus echoed the divine song.

But to please their father, Zeus, the Muses often stayed at his side and lulled him with their songs. At the symposia of the gods, on Olympus, their sweet and lovely voices sang of all that had passed, all that was passing and all that was yet to pass. They recalled the noble stock from which the gods had sprung – Mother Earth and Uranus, the boundless blue sky; they sang of the mighty deeds of the gods; then finally they joined their voices in a hymn of praise to their father, ruler of gods and men. And whenever they did this, a happy smile would spread across Zeus' face.

Yet they never forgot ordinary men, and their songs also praised those who, by their arts, their wisdom or their heroic

deeds, had done honour to the human race.

With the coming of the Muses, the sufferings of mankind were greatly relieved. It is even said that when the Muses were born and music came into the world, some people were so bewitched that they sang day and night, and could not bring themselves to stop even to eat or sleep, but went on singing until they died. Yet death stole upon them without pain, and they did not descend into the dark kingdom of Hades. Instead they became crickets. And ever since, these tiny creatures have been troubled neither by hunger nor thirst, but live only for their song and go on singing until they die.

The crickets love the Muses dearly, and often, when we believe them to be singing, they are really deep in talk with the nine sisters. Among other things, they tell them about men – who loves poetry and who song, and who loves the Muses

most of all.

Each of the nine sisters helped all artists according to the kind of art they loved. One inspired heroic songs, another hymns to the gods, and yet another dance and music.

Calliope was the first and most revered of the nine sisters. She was the Muse of epic and heroic poetry. It was Calliope whom Homer called upon in the first verse of the Iliad, with the words: "Sing, goddess, of the awful anger of Achilles". Artists adored her and drew her with a pen in her hand.

Erato was the next of the Muses. Her theme was love poetry and she played the lyre. Then came Polymnia, who was always shown with a thoughtful look on her face. She was the Muse of sacred hymns. After her was Euterpe, with her twin pipes, the Muse of lyrical song.

Two other Muses were devoted to the theatre: Thaleia, who

held a smiling mask in her hand, and was the Muse of comedy, and Melpomene, who carried a woe-begone mask and was the Muse of tragedy. Both of them were among the followers of Dionysus.

The Muse of dance was Terpsichore, and she, like Erato, carried a lyre.

The last two sisters concerned themselves chiefly with the sciences. They were Clio, Muse of history, whose song was the deeds of heroes and always carried a manuscript in her hand, and Urania, Muse of astronomy, who sang the glory of the stars and whose symbol was a globe.

These were the Muses: kind, hard-working and always ready to help man beautify his life.

But they were not alone in their efforts; for at their side stood three lovely goddesses who helped the Muses in their task, adding grace to beauty. And that is how they were named: the three Graces.

At the symposia of the gods they stood at Apollo's side, and when the divine notes of his lyre filled the palaces of Olympus, the three Graces and the nine Muses would spring to their feet to begin their dancing and songs.

But as soon as the revels on Olympus were ended, the Graces would hasten back to earth to be at man's side. Their task was a heavy but a noble one. They cast out cares, sweetened men's lives, and made happy events such as love, marriage and festivals even happier still. An ancient hymn says of them: "You make everything sweet and lovely. Thanks to you, poetry moves the hearts of men. With your aid, men become beautiful, wise and brave."

Everyone spoke their names with love and respect. They were the charming Aglaia, Euphrosyne, who loved and protected poets, and Thaleia, who adored music. They were three sisters as simple and direct as children, as pure as the lilies of the dawn and as lovely as the blossoming spring. They were the darlings of the gods, beloved of poets and singers, a favourite subject of sculptors and painters.

ORPHEUS AND EURYDICE

In those distant days when the Muses and the Graces made men's lives lovelier, there lived a great singer, poet and player whose name was Orpheus.

If anyone had asked, then, who was the most famous man in the world, he would not have been given the name of some king, or some great general or mighty hero. "No," the answer would have been: "Orpheus is the best-known and best-loved man in the world today."

The most incredible tales were told of Orpheus, and the magic powers of this singer and his songs.

One only had to say: "I have heard Orpheus" and a crowd

would gather, envious and admiring, demanding to hear of the great singer and his entrancing voice, the like of which the world had never heard before.

"Is it true," people would ask, "that when Orpheus sings the birds fall silent and the wild beasts gather around him? Is it true that his voice can move stones and that even the trees tear themselves from the ground and walk on their roots to be near him?"

And the answer would always be the same, confident and convincing: "When you, too, hear the voice of Orpheus, you will believe all that and much more besides. If you go to the town of Zoni, in Thrace, ask them to show you the oaks of Orpheus, which is the name they give to a group of trees that really look as if they are dancing. The trees have remained in that position ever since they heard Orpheus singing and play-ing his lyre. Orpheus' song can even calm the raging sea and his voice is so strong it can be heard over the roar of Zeus thunderclaps."

Such tales and many more were told of the great singer and, indeed, whoever was lucky enough to hear him – even if it was only once – immediately believed all the stories he had previously been told.

Orpheus was born in Thrace. His mother was the Muse Calliope and his father Oeagrus, king of Thrace. It was from his mother he inherited his love of poetry and song. His lyre was a gift from the god Apollo, and he was taught the art of playing it by the Muses themselves.

Lyre in hand, Orpheus would wander from village to village and town to town, singing in palaces and hovels alike. He sang of love, the mother of life, recounted the mighty deeds of heroes and sang the praises of those who had given their lives in noble causes.

Though his music filled his hearers with feelings beyond the power of words to describe, none was as moved, and none took greater pleasure in them than Orpheus himself. When he played to a large audience, Orpheus literally battled to achieve perfection. He wore himself out, suffered untold agonies, but always attained the unattainable. And then he would feel the overwhelming pleasure which was the reward for his noble efforts.

But every delight Orpheus had ever known was transformed into a happiness more wonderful still from the day he married Eurydice and they became the best-matched and most loving couple the world has ever known.

Aphrodite's winged son, Eros, had succeeded in binding the young couple in that loveliest of bondage, the ties of great and pure love.

Orpheus' art now soared to new heights. "There is nothing more lovely than true and well-matched love," he sang; and thanks to Eurydice his tender feelings, rooted in the joy of their shared lives, blossomed and flowered in countless unforgettable melodies.

Like all lovers, Orpheus and Eurydice sometimes wanted to be alone, to wander far afield and enjoy each other's company without a care in the world. They would often sit on a lonely hillside, and as they gazed on the lovely scenery spread below them, Orpheus would take up his lyre while Eurydice sang softly of the great and endless love which had brought them such happiness.

One day the young couple were strolling in the Vale of Tempe. The beauty of their surroundings was breathtaking. On the one side loomed the towering peaks of Olympus and on the other Mount Ossa, while between the two flowed the peaceful waters of the River Peneios, its banks overhung by age-old sycamores. Sitting in the deep shade at the foot of one of these trees, Orpheus leaned against its trunk and strummed the strings of his lyre while Eurydice danced and sang without a care in the world.

Orpheus and Eurydice felt as if they could stay in that spot for ever. Their hearts overflowed with joy at the loveliness around them. They wanted to reach out and embrace all nature. The gods, it seemed, had given the young lovers a more than generous share of happiness.

Alas! That happiness would soon be bitter ashes. For those three stern sisters, the Fates had decided that here the lovers' idyll must end. The thread of life which Clotho had woven for Eurydice stretched only to this point, and the lot which her sister Lachesis had picked out warned of a poisonous bite in the hour of Eurydice's greatest happiness.

And stern Atropos, who never permits the slightest change in what her sisters have decreed, wrote down Eurydice's cruel fate unmoved, in letters that could never be unwritten.

Why such unfairness?

Do the gods not know that when the greatest happiness is shattered its lace is taken by the most unbearable grief? Why should such harsh blows fall on those who deserve reward, not punishment?

But it seems that the gods have their own concerns, and cannot always watch over the petty affairs of mortals.

For while Eurydice skipped and danced happily around Orpheus as he played his lyre and sang, she stepped, unknowingly, on a serpent's lair and immediately a great snake darted out and sank its fangs into her foot.

Eurydice gave a heart-rending cry. Orpheus broke off his song in mid-note and ran to his beloved with cold fear striking at his heart.

The sight that greeted him was worse than his eyes dared believe: the pallor of death was spreading rapidly over Eurydice's face. She stretched out her arms in a despairing attempt to cling to her lover, but the poison had already coursed through her veins, and before Orpheus could take her outstretched arms in his, his darling Eurydice fell dead upon the ground.

Thus, in a single moment, a dream was shattered. Eurydice went down to the underworld, to the terrible kingdom of Hades, and Orpheus was left alone, unable to bear the pangs of his intolerable suffering.

Nothing could console him for the cruel loss of his beloved. As for his lyre, while its notes were too weak to bring him consolation, they were more than powerful enough to make his grief overflow. Whenever he picked up the instrument, his fingers plucked savagely at its strings, producing wild chords like thunderclaps in a raging storm, the outpourings of all the great singer's desperate unhappiness.

Nine days passed and nine nights, and nothing could soften Orpheus' terrible misery. And on the tenth day a thought took root in his mind that no mortal upon earth had ever dared to think before: he would descend into the dreadful kingdom of the shades to bring back his loved one.

A mere singer is no Heracles, perhaps, and hardly merits the name of hero. Yet the love of Orpheus for Eurydice and the cruel way he had lost her gave him the courage and the daring of a second Heracles – courage to attempt the impossible. He resolved to go down into Hades while still alive and beg Pluto, king of the underworld, for the return of the one who had been so unjustly taken from him: his Eurydice.

Armed only with his lyre, he set off on a journey too fearful for most men even to contemplate.

He searched far and wide. He asked wise men and seers –

...In a single moment, a dream was shattered...

but they all shook their heads:

"No, Orpheus, do not go. Dark Hades is not for the living."

"Even the dead find it hard to bear, and they all long endlessly to see the light of day once more."

"Pluto is stern and unbending, and Cerberus, who keeps ceaseless watch over the gates of the underworld, will never let you bring your loved one back again."

"You are not the only man in the world to lose someone he loved, Orpheus. Many have wept before you; many have felt that the pain of their loss would tear them apart; but little by little time dried their tears and healed their wounds. Man's fate is a hard one, and there is no-one who can change it."

But Orpheus paid no attention to any of this.

"That was not the answer I was seeking," he would reply. "Show me the road which leads to Hades."

And so, by repeated questioning, he learned that on the flanks of Mount Taygetus, in the Peloponnese, there is a gorge leading to a dark cave which Heracles had once descended into to bring up Cerberus, the unsleeping guardian of Hades, a hideous three-headed dog with a tail which ended in a dragon's mouth.

It was a fearsome path that led to the underworld. The closer Orpheus got to the gorge, the wilder and more deserted the countryside became.

The last man whom Orpheus saw on his way called out to

him:

"Hey! Where are you going? Turn back! No mortal ever takes that road, and no man ever steps inside that gorge. We would rather not set eyes on it, or even think about it."

But Orpheus entered the gorge and pressed on between the towering crags as if he had not heard a word. It was a landscape in which nothing grew but thorns and no creatures lived but snakes, but the strength of his love for Eurydice gave Orpheus the boldness and determination he needed to step over the threshold of Hades.

The further Orpheus went, the bleaker and more unwelcoming the scenery became, but he continued on his way until he reached the end of the terrible gorge and found himself facing a yawning black hole.

Any other man would have recoiled on seeing the fearsome gate of Hades, but Orpheus pressed on resolutely, and passed from the brightest daylight into the deepest darkness.

He had not gone forward many steps before he felt his hand caught in a firm grasp, and at the same moment an unearthly light sprang up around him. Turning his head, he saw a handsome man who held a rod round which were twined two snakes. On his head he wore a winged cap, and there were wings on his heels, too. Orpheus realized that the figure at his side was Hermes, the god who often came at Zeus' orders to lead the dead down to the underworld.

"I admire your courage, Orpheus," said Hermes, "but you

have set out to achieve the impossible. The king of the dead is hard and unyielding and does not know the meaning of human pain. True, he lets Adonis return to earth every spring, but only because he is loved by Aphrodite, and even so he takes him back again each autumn. He makes no other exceptions, unless you include Persephone, his wife – and anyway, she is not dead, but an immortal goddess who returns to her mother each year by order of Zeus himself. So do not hope for that which can never be. Let me lead you back to the world of men."

"Lead me to Pluto, the king of Hades," was Orpheus' reply. And in his voice there was such determination that Hermes stood in silence for a moment, and then led Orpheus onward again, still holding his hand.

Their path led through a long cave which went down and down. They went on for hours, winding ever deeper into the bowels of the earth.

At last, through the utter silence that reigned around them, came the faint, rhythmic sound of water lapping against rocks. Orpheus peered ahead and saw that they were approaching the banks of an underground river. It was the Styx, the sacred river of Hades.

A ferryman was rowing his boat across the water towards them. This was Charon, come to pick up the shade of Orpheus, or so he thought, and ferry him over to the kingdom of Pluto on the other side. But when he saw a living man, he was so taken aback that he cried out angrily to Hermes:

"Don't you know that I take no living passengers aboard my boat! What have you brought him here for?"

"It was my own decision to come here," replied Orpheus boldly. "Now, will you be kind enough to let me over? I wish to appear before the king of the underworld."

"And I know why," retorted Charon. "So you can plead with him and beg favours. I wonder why you went to the trouble of such a journey, when you know you're no more likely to persuade me than you are my master, Pluto. Now, get out of my sight before I give you one with my oar and make you wish you'd never been so insolent. Go back to the world above and wait your turn to die, if you want me to carry you over."

While Charon was addressing these angry words to him, Orpheus unslung the lyre from his shoulder as if he had not heard, and brushed his fingers across its strings. Never before had the dark halls of Hades echoed to such bewitching notes.

"What sounds are these?" cried Charon in wonder, secretly hoping that Orpheus would go on playing.

And indeed, the hard-hearted ferryman had scarcely time to complete his thought before the notes of the lyre flooded the air once more, and Charon stood leaning on his oar as if a spell had bound him.

Then, never lifting his fingers from the strings, Orpheus moved slowly forward and stepped into the boat, followed by the wondering Hermes. Charon stood listening, motionless, for a few moments longer, then, raising the oar in both hands, he pushed off from the rocky shore and sent the boat gliding smoothly and silently across the sacred waters.

Entranced by the beguiling notes of Orpheus' lyre, Charon steered his boat over to the great gate of Hades, which loomed ahead. This gate always, stood wide open, but it was guarded eternally by Cerberus. Hermes and Orpheus walked through. When Cerberus saw the god coming in with a living man, he could hardly believe his eyes. A deep growl welled from his three throats, and the dragon's head on the tip of his tail shrieked hideously. But that was all; for the task of Cerberus was to prevent the dead from leaving, and not to close the gate on those who wished to enter.

Before long, Hermes and Orpheus were standing in the presence of Pluto, the god who ruled the underworld. He was seated on a tall, imposing throne. At his side sat his wife, the lovely Persephone, while on his left, on other raised thrones, sat the three wise judges of Hades: Minos, Rhadamanthys and Aeacus, whose task was to pass sentence on the dead for the crimes they had committed during their lives.

They all rose in surprise when they saw Hermes leading a living man into the underworld. Pluto's face darkened with rage, and he was about to hurl a furious question at Hermes when the superb strains of Orpheus' lyre filled the air, and the great singer's voice broke into a song of compelling beauty.

Pluto stood silent and ecstatic. The god whose ears heard
nothing but the groans of the dead was now held spellbound
by the voice of Orpheus himself, the greatest singer the world
had ever known.

But if the sounds moved Pluto, they plucked an even deeper
chord in Persephone's heart, bringing back memories of the
lovely, flower-decked earth above, its bird-song and the bab-
ble of its crystal brooks, and of its singers who, with lyre and
flute, made melodies to praise life's joys and give thanks to
the gods.

The judges of the dead listened with the same hushed rev-
erence, recalling the beauty of life in the world above. Stern
Minos, the mighty king of Crete, was moved almost to tears.
Just Aeacus, king of Aegina, choked back a sob; while
Rhadamanthys, the great lawmaker and king of Boeotia, listened in ecstasy. Mighty lords though they might be in Hades,
they knew how much happier was a slave's lot in the world
above.

And so Orpheus sang on, his voice stirring waves of longing in his listeners' hearts. His verses told of the joys of life
on earth, of love, the great gift of the gods, then they recounted
his passion for Eurydice, and finally they poured out all his
pain at the unjust loss of his beloved. And as his voice grew
stronger, so did the emotions it aroused, spreading like rip-
ples to the furthest reaches of dark Hades.

The shades of the dead heard Orpheus' heart-rending song

and ceased their groaning. Tantalus, punished for his insolence to the gods by the pangs of hunger and thirst, forgot for
a while his dreadful sufferings and listened spellbound.
Sisyphus, who was paying the penalty of his evil deeds on
earth by forever heaving a huge boulder up a mountainside,
paused from his back-breaking labours to listen to Orpheus'
song; and the Danaids, whose crimes in the world above now
condemned them to pour water endlessly into a huge, bottomless urn, halted their futile task for a space and listened
with bursting hearts.

But suddenly, from among the ranks of the dead, the shade
of a young woman ran forward. It was Eurydice, who hearing
Orpheus' song now flew to meet her loved one. And a moment later the law of untold ages was shattered: the shade of
Eurydice threw itself into the arms of the living Orpheus.

Pluto looked on thunderstruck; for the act he now beheld
was an open challenge to the sacred and eternal laws which
separate the living from the dead.

And all who saw it feared that in an outburst of terrible
rage Pluto would put a violent and horrible end to this scene
of unheard of courage and beauty which they now witnessed.

Deeply moved, but fearing that Pluto's wrath would break
upon him, too, Hermes begged the lovers to release each other
from their passionate embrace. And the young couple at once
did as he bid.

Now all eyes were on Pluto, waiting to see how the stern

god's rage would vent itself.

Yet Pluto only hung his head and remained silent. After a long pause, he lifted it again and gazed at Persephone, whose lovely eyes were brimming with tears.

And then he turned to Orpheus and spoke:

"Tell me what favour you desire, and I shall grant it to you. I swear this by the holy waters of the Styx!"

"Mighty lord of the underworld," replied Orpheus, "I want you to give me back my beloved Eurydice. Her days in the fair world above were all too few, and when love came to her, she had no time to taste its joys. I cannot bear to think of her suffering in the dark depths of Hades. I cannot live without Eurydice, nor she without me."

"It shall be as you desire, Orpheus, just as I promised. But you, too, must give me a promise in return."

"Whatever you wish, mighty lord", replied Orpheus.

"Eurydice may leave with you now. You will go ahead, and she will follow. But you will not turn your head to look at her before you reach the light of day. If you do so before then, Eurydice will return to my kingdom at that very instant."

Pluto's terms were hard, but Orpheus accepted them willingly, overjoyed to think that once they had climbed up into the sunlight again he would have won his loved one back for ever.

They set off. Hermes led the way, followed by Orpheus, while a little behind them came Eurydice. When they reached the gates, Cerberus reared his three heads threateningly, but as soon as Orpheus brushed his fingers against the strings of his lyre and its lovely melodies filled the air with their glorious notes, the fearsome guardian of Hades lowered his heads and stood silent and unmoving, bewitched by the sounds he heard.

Thus they passed through the gates of Hades, crossed over the Styx once more on Charon's ferry and started back up the long and rising path that led through the cavern. The way was hard and tiring, but none of them gave it a thought. Orpheus' thoughts were fastened upon Eurydice, who was following somewhere behind him. But was she following? This was the terrible doubt which slowly took root in Orpheus' mind. For in the silence of death which reigned about them he could hear his own steps, he could hear the steps of Hermes going on ahead, but from behind he could hear nothing. Why?

"What if Eurydice is not coming? What if Cerberus would not let her pass through the gates of Hades? What if Charon refused to let her on board his ferry?"

"Ah, if only I knew that Eurydice were following me! If only I could see her or hear something!" The thought tortured him constantly all along the way. And the way was endless.

They were in thick darkness, but Orpheus could still make out the form of Hermes in front of him. If that were so, he only had to turn his head and he would be able to see if Eurydice were there behind.

"But what am I thinking?" cried Orpheus, as he realized where such thoughts were leading him. "Oh, Gods, if only I knew whether Eurydice is coming, and whether I shall see her when we reach the light! But I do not know. Why do I hear nothing? Nothing! Why?"

A prey to his fears, Orpheus followed in the footsteps of the god, his heart close to bursting with his terrible anxiety.

At last, a faint glimmer of reflected daylight appeared in the distance. Orpheus' anguish rose to breaking point. With each step, the light grew stronger, but as it did, so Orpheus' doubts grew more unbearable.

Bright light now flooded the cave. Their journey was within moments of its end. Before them shone the light of day. Only seconds now, and Orpheus would have won his loved one back for ever. If she was behind him!

"But if she isn't?" thought Orpheus bleakly – and turned his head. And saw Eurydice.

Ah, why are the gods so hard on man?

In an agony of despair, Orpheus stretched out his arms to embrace his loved one. But too late. Before he could touch her, she slipped from his grasp like a withered leaf caught by the autumn wind, and was whirled back to the dark kingdom of the shades.

This second loss was still more shattering than the first. Orpheus ran headlong after Eurydice in his desperation, but she had already vanished from his sight. Soon he found him-

self on the banks of the Styx once more and begged Charon on bended knees to carry him across. But he might as well have saved his breath, for the ferryman turned a deaf ear to his pleas. Seven days and seven nights he paced the banks of the Styx, pleading with Charon to row him to the other side, and on the eighth, vain, day he took the dark path once again and climbed the hard, steep way until he found himself once more in the light above, and in despair.

There, at the mouth of the cave, he found the lyre which had slipped from his nerveless grasp in that moment of horror when he had stretched out his hands to clutch at Eurydice.

It was cruel beyond belief! The fallen lyre lay just two steps from the light of the sun!

Orpheus bent down and took it up. Torn by grief, he crashed his hand across its chords, and the pain of his misery echoed and re-echoed through the savage mountains like a raging storm. Now, nothing could bring him consolation. Orpheus had lost his loved one for a second time because he could not accept the harsh terms imposed upon him by stern Pluto.

The unhappy singer returned to his homeland. Months went by, and then years, but Eurydice still haunted his waking dreams. Many people advised him to marry again, but in reply he would only pick up his lyre and play melodies so mournful that they broke the hearts of the very stones that echoed them.

At last, when the great feasts in honour of Dionysus were being held in Thrace, the time came for this great and tragic singer to meet his end.

The Dionysiac festivals were attended mainly by women, who drank till the wine spilled from their lips, and danced and sang in imitation of the Maenads, the wild nymphs of Dionysus' train. These women invited Orpheus to play and sing for them, but he was too miserable and sick at heart for dancing and such revels.

The women were offended by his refusal and left in anger, but when they returned from the festival, drunken and riotous, they met Orpheus on the road once more.

"Here's the fellow who insulted us!" they shrieked, "the one who hates us! the one who refused to honour Dionysus!" and with these words they began to attack him with rocks, with wooden staves, and even with sickles.

And so, their heads reeling from the fumes of the wine, hardly knowing what it was they did, they fell on the unhappy singer like savage beasts and tore him limb from limb.

When the women came to their senses and realized what a hideous crime they had committed, they went to the nearest river to wash the blood from their hands, and with it the shame of their deed. But the river suddenly dried up. The river god had led its waters away underground so he would not have to share in their guilt.

Orpheus died, but his soul sped gladly to Hades, where it was reunited with Eurydice.

Now Orpheus could at last gaze on his beloved with no fear that he might lose her once again. The joys of life were unknown in the dark kingdom of the shades; there was neither laughter nor joy in Hades, and no sound of lyre or melodious voice broke the silence of the underworld; yet Orpheus and Eurydice were happy there, if no one else was. For their love had defeated death itself.

And Orpheus' art, too, had won a similar victory.

On a wooded slope of Olympus, there is a spot where the birds sing more sweetly than anywhere else in the world. For it was here that the Muses buried Orpheus' body. But his lyre was borne by the waves to the island of Lesbos where it was washed up upon the shore, and, as the waves beat rhythmically against its chords, the lyre played sweet melodies. Its song was heard by Apollo, who came and took it up from the sea's margin and placed it high in the heavens; and ever since, it has shone as the bright constellation called The Lyre.

Years went by, yet still the waves kept up their sweet, rhyth-

mic song as they beat upon the rocky headlands and the sandy
coves of that lovely island. And this is why its people have
kept their love of music and poetry, and have produced such
great poets and singers as Sappho, Alcaeus and Arion.

There is a delightful and unusual story about Arion which
is well worth telling. According to this myth, Arion was the
son of the god of the sea, the earth-shaker Poseidon. From his
earliest youth he distinguished himself as a poet and musician, and one day he happened to catch the attention of
Periander, ruler of Corinth and one of the seven sages of an-
tiquity. Now Periander was a great patron of the arts, and
when he heard Arion he was as entranced by his voice as by
the verses of his song and his melodious playing. Deeply
moved, he invited this marvellous singer to come to Corinth,
which was then a rich and powerful city where artists of all
kinds enjoyed Periander's generous support.

Arion accepted, and thanks to his move to Corinth he won
such fame that soon his name was known in every corner of
the earth.

One year, a great festival of the arts was held in Sicily. All
the cities of the ancient world sent their brightest talent to
compete, and Corinth chose Arion.

In Sicily, Arion's performances were a triumphal progress.
Wherever he appeared he was wildly applauded. The judges
never had any difficulty in deciding whom the victor's prize

should go to. As composer, poet and player he won the first award in every town and festival he appeared at. And when the day came for him to return to Greece he had with him a whole treasury of gold cups and other gifts of priceless value.

But Arion was destined to fall among thieves. For the ship which was to carry him back to Corinth had hardly set sail when the captain, flanked by two burly sailors, marched up to the young singer and told him with a cruel laugh that they were going to throw him overboard.

"But what crime am I guilty of?" asked Arion in amazement. "What have I done to deserve such a fate?"

"If you really want to know, I'll tell you: you're carrying more gold than is good for you."

"As for the gold, you're welcome to it," replied Arion. "But at least spare my life, so that I can go on singing."

"We're not stupid enough to do you that favour," returned the captain. "For as soon as we reach Corinth you will tell Periander we have robbed you, and then it will be all up with us. Between you and me, I'd do the same thing myself if anybody were fool enough to strip me of my wealth but spare my life."

Yet even these harsh words did not make Arion lose hope.

"I see I cannot persuade you to grant me my life," he replied, "but you must at least do me this personal favour: before I die, let me play my lyre one last time."

"Play, sing – dance if you like!" was the captain's callous

answer.

And so Arion sat in the stern of the boat and began to play his lyre and sing, calling on his father, the great god of the sea, to come and help him.

The melody that wafted over the waves was lovely beyond belief, and soon a whole school of listening dolphins was following the ship. But the captain was quite unmoved by the song and suddenly gave the great singer a savage kick which sent him tumbling into the sea below. Then, without sparing a glance behind him, he made a beeline for Arion's sea-chest, anxious to set eyes on the treasure which had fallen into his hands – or which he thought had fallen.

For Arion had not drowned, after all. Seeing him sinking, one of the dolphins had immediately dived beneath him and borne his body up upon the waves. And soon the sweet airs of Arion's lyre rang out over the waters once more as the singer continued his voyage back to Greece seated upon the back of a dolphin.

The friendly creatures put Arion ashore at Tainaron in the Peloponnese and from there he managed to reach Corinth ahead of the robbers. As soon as he reached the city, he went straight to Periander and told him of his grim experience and how he had been saved.

The next day, the robbers' ship put into harbour and Periander summoned the captain to his palace to hear what had become of Arion.

...For Arion had not drowned, after all...

The captain, of course, had rehearsed his answer:

"He wished to stay on in Sicily for a while, your majesty, and so we sailed without him."

"Do you swear to this?" asked the king. And what could the robber captain do but give his oath?

But at that very moment, a door opened and Arion appeared! The captain reeled in amazement. He could not believe his eyes!

"But this is not possible!" he gasped.

"And yet it is!" roared Periander. And he immediately ordered his soldiers to seize the man and bind him.

Bound hand and foot, the captain was thrown on board a ship which immediately put out to sea; and there, on Periander's orders, he was thrown over the side.

In his case, there was no miracle to save him.

While we are on the subject of music and musicians, here is one last myth – that of Marsyas the satyr, who lost his life because he dared to pit his skill in music against Apollo by challenging him with his flute.

But that flute had a story behind it, and if Marsyas had known the story, he would surely never have put the instrument to his lips. This is how the tale goes:

One day, the goddess Athena found the beautiful, long, thigh bone of a deer. It was a pleasing object, and she wanted to make something both attractive and useful from it. She soon decided what she would make, and began to work on the bone with great care and art. She cut off both ends, cleaned it out well inside and then drilled holes down its length. Finally, she fashioned a handsome mouthpiece at the top. When she had finished, she placed the mouthpiece between her lips and began to blow, placing her fingers on the holes and lifting them. Lovely sounds came from the instrument she had created. It was the world's first flute.

The goddess was enchanted with her new creation and never tired of playing it. On one occasion, however, when she was playing for the other gods of Olympus, she noticed that Hera and Aphrodite were staring at her and exchanging secret giggles.

Athena put down her flute and shouted angrily:

"Why make fun of me? Everyone else is enjoying my music, and you sit there laughing!"

"If only you could see your face when you blow into that thing, you'd understand why we're laughing," replied the two goddesses.

"They must be jealous of me," muttered Athena, and went off to play her flute by the banks of a river, where she could see her own reflection as she blew. But when she saw how her cheeks puffed out and her lovely face became distorted by the effort of blowing, she realized that Hera and Aphrodite could not be blamed for laughing behind their hands, and in a sudden burst of anger she hurled the flute away, shouting:

"Miserable toy! Because of you I am insulted. A curse on anyone who picks you up and puts you to his lips."

The flute which Athena had thrown away was found by Marsyas, and, suspecting nothing of the curse, he picked it up, liked the look of it and decided to keep it. In time, he grew fond of the flute and learned to play it so well that whoever heard him said that not even Apollo could play as well.

How was unlucky Marsyas to know that the curse of Athena hung over him? He had never been one to boast, but now he began to tell everyone that he could make even better music than golden-haired Apollo.

It was not long before the great god of music appeared before the unlucky satyr. He was magnificently attired, and under his arm he carried his golden lyre. The nine Muses accompanied the shining god.

"How dare you call yourself a better player than me?" Apollo demanded. "Can there be anyone in the world, god or mortal, whose skill in music is a match for mine?"

"All we need do is put it to the test," replied Marsyas coolly. "Let your nine sisters judge which of us plays better. But whoever wins may impose any punishment he wishes upon the loser."

Foolish Marsyas, what rash words were these? Did you imagine that a mere satyr could pit his poor skills against a mighty god? And did you not know that the immortals are not to be insulted, and are cruel beyond belief when they wish to exact punishment? For Apollo's answer was swift and terrible:

"I shall defeat you and skin you alive for your insolence!" he screamed, his face flushed with rage.

But Marsyas seemed quite unconcerned, and putting the flute to his lips, began to play. The Muses stood listening in awe. Even Apollo thought his ears were deceiving him. For the music which flowed from Marsyas' flute was so perfect that neither god nor man could better it. Next, it was Apollo's turn, but though his music was as good as Marsyas' in every way, it was not better.

And so the Muses were unable to declare either of them the winner.

By now, Apollo was boiling with rage. He was determined to be revenged upon the satyr who had belittled him – by fair means or foul.

"Very well," he snarled, "now we shall play with our instruments upside-down!"

And holding his lyre the other way up, he played it as superbly as before. But a flute, alas, cannot be played with its mouthpiece pointing downwards, and poor Marsyas could not coax a single note from his instrument.

And so the Muses declared Apollo the winner.

The god's revenge came down on Marsyas like a thunderbolt, and the poor satyr died in hideous agony because he had dared to challenge an immortal.

The wood-nymphs wept for Marsyas and buried him by a river. The Muses felt sorry for the unlucky satyr and begged their father Zeus to take pity on him. The ruler of gods and men listened to their pleas, so Marsyas did not descend to the dark depths of Hades. Instead, his spirit was released into the waters of the river which flowed by his grave. Ever since, the waters of the River Marsyas have flowed as musically as if they were indeed playing a flute, and men have listened to its song with pleasure. But when the river remembers Apollo's cruel revenge, its waters swell with wrath and roar wild threats, spreading fear and sorrow in their path.

THE GODS OF THE WINDS

In the old days, whenever the frozen north wind blew in savage blasts, people would say that once again some mortal had enraged Boreas, the mighty winged god who lived in a tall, white castle in the mountains of Thrace.

The castle of Boreas was fair and stately, and the god spent most of his time there. But if ever he got into a rage, he would launch himself from his snowy palace and with great beats of his powerful wings swoop down on the houses of men, bringing frosts, tempests and snowstorms as he came.

Yet Boreas was not always savage and wild: he could also be calm and patient.

He showed how great his patience was when Erechtheus, king of Athens, promised that he would give the god his lovely daughter Oreithyia as a wife. To tell the truth, Erechtheus did not make this promise willingly, for he had no desire to marry off the youngest of his four daughters. He had already found husbands for the other three, but he wished to keep Oreithyia at his side.

Erechtheus let no man set eyes on the beautiful girl. He would not even allow her out of the palace. From the window of her chamber, Oreithyia could see only the sky and nothing more. And so it seemed certain that she would never marry and would never leave her father, whom, for all his harshness, she loved dearly.

But one summer day, when Oreithyia opened her window to let in some fresh air, a gentle little north wind caressed her face and ruffled her golden hair. She breathed in its freshness and smiled up at the cloudless sky, her face radiant with beauty.

At that moment Boreas flew past the open window and caught sight of the lovely princess. The winged god fell in love with her on the spot, and without wasting a moment he hastened to her father and begged to let him marry her and take her back to his snowy palace.

It is difficult for a mortal to refuse his daughter's hand to a god, even if that mortal happens to be a king. And it was a thousand times more difficult to refuse Boreas. For no one could resist the fury of the god who commanded the most violent of winds, and disaster could strike the palace of the king if he dared say no.

And so Erechtheus was afraid to deny the winged god. Yet on the other hand, he had no wish to give away his daughter. Finally, pretending to be both pleased and flattered, he said:

"I give you my daughter gladly, Boreas, and I am moved by the honour you have shown me. However, I would like a little time to get her used to the idea, for she has become so accustomed to living alone with her parents that I don't know how she will receive your offer."

"I am delighted to see you are so willing," replied the god. "And much as I would like to take the princess with me now, I shall give you the time that you need. I shall come back for her one month from today."

As soon as the month was up, Boreas returned.

"All is well," Erechtheus told him. "I have persuaded her. But she would like a little time to prepare herself – not leave home just like that. You know what I mean."

In fact, Boreas did not quite know what the king meant. But he decided to be patient for another month and left empty-handed.

When he came back again, Erechtheus said:

"Everything is ready. I have prepared her for her departure. You can take her with you immediately. Only, her mother is ill, and Oreithyia would be very upset if she had to leave with her in this state. You do see my point, don't you?"

Boreas did not see the king's point at all, and suspected that something was amiss. But he pretended to agree, and left yet again without Oreithyia.

When Erechtheus saw how easy-going Boreas was, he became more confident – or, rather, overconfident, and when the god returned once more the king of Athens told him:

"Look, we've talked it all over, we've agreed, nothing stands in the way and as I've told you before, I consider it a great personal honour that you're taking my daughter as your wife. But I've been thinking things over and I'd like to tell you something for your own good. To tell you the truth, I think you're taking a girl who's rather too young. Wouldn't you do better to wait till she's grown up a little, and is more fit to be your wife and helpmate, and a real mother to your children? Come back in a year or two, and we'll talk it over. Don't tell me that you'll find some other girl in the meantime and forget our little Oreithyia, eh?" And emboldened by his own words, Erechtheus gave Boreas a hearty slap on the back, laughing cunningly to himself.

By now, Boreas saw everything. It was as clear as daylight! Erechtheus didn't want to give away his daughter at all, and each of his requests for delay had been sheer trickery. Yet in spite of his terrible fury, the god of the north wind held himself in check and allowed none of his feelings to show.

"Very well, I shall think it over," he replied, and departed. He soared high into the clouds, his spirits in a turmoil of rage.

Erechtheus had insulted him beyond endurance and the thought of losing Oreithyia was not to be borne.

"What does Erechtheus take me for?" Boreas growled. "It's my own fault for sitting and listening to his excuses for so long; I, who can raise such winds from the north that they tear up hundred-year-old oaks by the roots and flatten lofty cypresses! I, who can whip the ocean waves into towering mountains and lash the earth with hail at will, bringing snow and frost, and freezing water as hard as stone! I, whose wrath men tremble at, to be humbled by Erechtheus and sit there weakly begging his favours like some poor, common mortal! No! I, and I alone, shall decide! I shall take Oreithyia by force and make her my wife!"

With these words he gave a mighty beat of his great wings, and in an instant a fearsome storm broke upon the earth. The north wind howled wildly, wreaking havoc in its path. With one terrifying blast it struck the palace of Erechtheus, hurling all its doors wide open, and in with it came the winged god, a force no man could resist. Snatching up Oreithyia in his strong arms, he soared off with her high into the heavens.

Soon, the wind dropped and to the earth there came the calm which follows a storm. The anger of Boreas softened into love and the mighty god held his precious burden in a tender embrace as he flew joyfully towards Thrace.

Boreas held a great wedding feast and Oreithyia became mistress of the snowy palace of the mightiest of the gods of the wind. She gave her husband two sons who became fine young men, winged like their father. Their names were Zetes and Calais and they took part in the expedition of the Argonauts, performing many great feats.

Boreas' brothers were the other great winds of the earth: the South wind which brought life-giving rain; Zephyrus, who blew cool and gentle from the West and was loved by all men, and Eurus, a soft and refreshing wind from the East.

The ruler of all these winds was Aeolus.

Aeolus lived happily with his wife, his six sons and his six daughters in an imposing palace on an island off the coast of Italy. In those days it was named Aeolia, but today men call it Stromboli.

Whenever he wished, Aeolus could forbid the winds to blow, and then peace reigned over the whole earth.

Long ago, when the war against Troy was coming to its end and the Greeks were returning to their homeland, the waves brought Odysseus, king of Ithaca, to the coast of Aeolia. Poseidon, the mighty ruler of the oceans, had cast the hero's ships onto the shore in his rage when he learned that Odysseus had blinded his son, the fearsome Cyclops, Polyphemus.

Aeolus welcomed Odysseus and his companions to his island. He ordered his six sons to help him repair their ships, and every evening they all gathered in his palace to eat, drink and make merry.

When the god of the winds heard of the misfortunes Odysseus had suffered in his wanderings, he took pity on him and decided to help him return to his native land without further misadventure.

When the time came for their ships to sail, Aeolus thought of a way to protect the mariners from the wrath of Poseidon. He went and slaughtered a large ox and made a bag from its hide; then he captured all the winds except Zephyrus, shut them up inside the bag, and tied it securely with a silver cord in case it came open and let the winds out.

"I am entrusting this to you," Aeolus told Odysseus. "Keep it on board, guard it well, and if you do not open it, you will be in Ithaca within ten days."

When they set sail, Odysseus forbade his companions to touch the bag, and Zephyrus swelled their sails and drove the ships swiftly eastwards towards Greece.

They made good speed for nine days, but on the tenth, when the ships were already nearing Ithaca, and Odysseus was asleep, his companions began to suspect that their leader was keeping something hidden from them.

"He's got treasure in that sack," said one.

"And that's why he's afraid we'll open it," added another.

"We've all fought and suffered together," protested a third, "and now he's hoarding a sack of gold and silver, while we're going home empty-handed."

"Let's open it," urged the first sailor.

"Yes, come on, open it!" they all shouted.

And open it they did.

So, when the mountains of Ithaca were already to be seen on the horizon, all the winds came jostling each other out of the bag, and a raging storm burst upon their heads. The sails were torn to shreds in an instant. The ships danced like corks on the waves and the gale drove them far from the shores of their native land and into regions where new and perilous adventures awaited them.

Ever since, whenever a sudden violent and destructive wind springs up, men say that Aeolus' bag has been opened.

As we know, Aeolus had six daughters. The most beautiful of these was Alcyone, whom he gave in marriage to Ceyx, king of Trachis.

Alcyone loved her husband dearly, and fear gnawed at her heart each time he sailed too far from shore in search of fish. But Ceyx was such a keen fisherman that nothing she said could hold him back.

But one day, Alcyone felt more than fear – a terrible foreboding that some awful fate would befall her husband, and she begged him not to sail into the open sea.

"I know the currents and the winds," was his reply. "My boat is a sturdy one and there is none can sail her like me. Besides, the weather is fine and it's too good a day to miss my fishing."

"I don't deny that you're a fine steersman," his wife replied, "and I know you understand the weather and the sea. But there have been times when even my father was caught unawares, even though he rules the winds. I've often heard him say that a raging storm can suddenly blow up in the calmest weather. So I beg you, listen to me for once, and don't put out to sea today."

Perhaps if Ceyx had seen the tears in his wife's eyes he would have done as she wished and not gone fishing. But his pride blinded him to her anguish, obvious though it was.

Such is life. Sometimes we do not even want to know how much pain we cause others, for fear of spoiling our own petty pleasures. And when the time comes to face the consequences, it is too late to be sorry.

The price which Ceyx paid for his selfish pride was a heavy one.

The weather broke without warning when he was far out at sea. A howling gale blew up, whipping the waters into sudden fury. Black clouds scudded across the horizon, hunted by winds which lashed the seas to foam. Within moments, the waves had become mountains – and Ceyx' boat was matchwood.

Alcyone ran desperately down to the shore and, clambering up a tall rock which looked out over the gulf, she anxiously strained her eyes for some sign of her beloved husband until finally she saw his body being carried in on the waves.

Alcyone was distraught. Now, there was nothing she wanted but to give Ceyx one last, passionate, embrace and then join him in death. Impelled by her own despair, she threw herself from the rock into the foaming sea below.

As Alcyone fulfilled her last wish, the gods took pity on her and Ceyx and turned them both into waterbirds. And ever since, they have been called halcyons, or kingfishers. These birds mate for life, and if death carries off the male, his companion tries to end her own life, just as Alcyone did.

Halcyons lay their eggs in the depths of winter; but if the chicks are to hatch the days must be sunny and no chill winds should blow. It is said that ever since Alcyone's time Aeolus has kept the winds in check at midwinter, to allow his daughter, and all other kingfishers, to raise their young in safety. It is a period of gentle and springlike weather in the heart of a bitter season and, even now, we call it "the halcyon days".

DAEDALUS AND ICARUS

From time immemorial man has longed to soar into the sky, but in the distant days which we are talking of it seemed impossible that this bold dream would ever come true.

And yet, mythology tells us that there was a man who not only believed in human flight but actually achieved it.

His name was Daedalus, and with him flew Icarus, his son.

How this came to happen is a story in itself. And the tale begins in Athens, city of wisdom and beauty.

Beneath the Acropolis, near the ancient market place, there were many workshops and studios in those days. In them worked a host of sculptors, painters and other kinds of artists. Outstanding among them was Daedalus, an artist and craftsman of consummate skill descended from the line of Erechtheus.

It is said that the statues Daedalus made were so lifelike that they seemed about to open their lips and speak. His paintings were equally true to life. Yet in spite of this, Daedalus was best known as an architect and inventor. His buildings made the lovely city of Athens fairer still, while among his inventions are counted the geometric compass, the drill, the axe and masts and sails for ships, all of which were significant discoveries for their time.

The people of Athens were so awed by Daedalus' achievements that they said he was taught and helped by Athena herself, goddess of wisdom and the fine arts.

But there were some who envied his talents and wished him ill. For while great men gather many friends around them, they also make enemies. And in this case, the enemies were able to do great harm to Athena's pupil, as we shall see.

Daedalus had an assistant in his workshop, his sister Perdix's fifteen-year-old son, Talos. A gifted and hard-working lad, he loved his uncle's work, listened carefully to his advice and became more skilful by the day.

One day, Talos wanted to cut a wooden rod in two, and he

decided to use the sharp-toothed jawbone of a snake which he had found not long before. The result was a cut so quick and clean it made him sit down and think seriously. In the end, he took a metal blade and filed teeth out of it, just like those on the snake's jaw he had used. With the tool he had made, he could now cut not merely a stick but a whole tree-trunk. And so the first saw came into the world.

Daedalus was impressed by the boy's achievement and proudly showed everyone the new tool which Talos had invented.

"Look, Perdix," he told his sister next day. "See what a clever tool your son has made! Come and see what we can cut now, with this!" And he showed her how beautifully Talos' saw could cut through wood.

"You should look to your laurels," said Perdix laughingly. "For it seems to me that one day Talos will be more than a match for you!"

"That is what I hope for and what I am working towards," replied Daedalus gravely.

But Talos was not destined to go any further along the road to fame.

One day, uncle and nephew were walking on the Acropolis. They were picking their way along the rim of the great rock, admiring the city far below and the plain of Attica beyond when, suddenly, disaster struck. Talos stumbled, missed his footing, and, before Daedalus could reach out to save him, he toppled from the edge and was killed.

This terrible mischance was seized on by Daedalus' enemies, evil and mean-minded men, but at the same time ones
who wielded great influence. They succeeded in having him
dragged before the courts, where they actually accused him
of pushing Talos to his death out of jealousy! Though if the
truth were known, it was they who were jealous of Daedalus
and afraid of the powers given him by his art.

Knowing they had friends among the judges, the accusers
shamelessly demanded the death sentence for Daedalus. They
did not achieve this aim, but did succeed in getting him banished from Athens for life, even though countless Athenians
knew how dearly the great man had loved his nephew, and
not one of them was ignorant of the fact that a true artist is
incapable of committing a criminal act.

Thus, one blow fell upon the other. A gifted helper and
future artist was lost for ever, and on top of the death of Talos
came a heavy and unjust sentence which deprived Daedalus
of the right to live and work in the city which had given him
birth.

Doubly embittered, the great artist took the path of exile.
He made his way down to Piraeus and boarded the first vessel which happened to be leaving port. Where it was bound
for, he neither knew nor cared. Not till they had left harbour
did he learn that his ship was sailing eastwards to the islands
of the Cyclades, calling at Delos, Naxos and Thera, and fi-

nally making its way south to the great island of Crete.

In those days, Crete was ruled by the hard-hearted Minos, son of Zeus by Europa. The Crete of king Minos was the mightiest power in the Mediterranean. Its fleet was the largest in the world and its empire at the height of its glory.

Untold wealth had been gathered into its capital, Cnossus, a city which glittered with gold. Luxurious palaces and temples had been raised, along with a host of other opulent and imposing buildings. For Minos was not a man to hide his wealth. He wanted every stranger who set foot on the island to be dazzled by his riches and power.

Minos prided himself on his achievements, but when he came to visit Athens and looked on its temples and statues, the grace of its public buildings and its other works of art, his pride in the show of wealth which adorned Cnossus evaporated immediately. It was then he realized, for the first time, that even if you have all the money in the world, you can create nothing beautiful with it unless you have the training and the instinct of an artist to guide your hand.

So, during his stay in Athens, whenever a particular work of art caught Minos' fancy, he would ask who had created it. And the answer he received would always be the same: Daedalus.

In this way, Minos learned of the greatest artist and inventive craftsman the world had ever known.

When the great king returned to Crete, overwhelmed by

his impressions of Athens, his homeland now seemed poor and mean to him, even if it was swimming in gold and feared by every nation upon earth.

"If I had a Daedalus of my own," he kept telling himself, "I should want nothing more in the world."

Then, one day, when he was sitting wrapped in gloomy thoughts upon his solid gold throne, a courtier came jubilantly into his presence.

"Hail, god-born king of mighty Crete!" the courtier cried. "I bring you news which will banish your gloom this very instant, and bring you great joy!"

"There's been nothing but good news recently," replied the king despondently, "but none so good it could shake off my sadness."

"But this time," insisted the courtier, "I believe you have gained what you desire above all things: Daedalus is in Crete, and seeks to enter your service! "

Minos jumped up. "Daedalus in Crete?" he cried joyfully. "I shall run to welcome him in person!"

And welcome him he did, with royal honours, immediately putting at Daedalus' disposal all the means he required to begin his task of beautifying Crete from the very next day.

Thus Cnossus and the rest of the island began to be adorned with graceful buildings and lovely works of art, and Minos could not praise Daedalus too highly.

Daedalus stayed and worked in Crete for many years. He married Naucrate, a lovely girl from the Cyclades, and she bore him a son, Icarus. But she died when the child was still very young.

From his earliest years Icarus learned to love building, painting and sculpture, and his greatest ambition was to follow in his father's footsteps. When he was coming into manhood he helped in the construction of the labyrinth, the greatest of the works which Daedalus undertook in Crete.

The labyrinth was a building of such complexity, with so many rooms and corridors, that whoever entered it could not find his way out again.

In the innermost part of the labyrinth was imprisoned the Minotaur, a man-eating monster with a human body and the head of a bull. This hideous beast was killed by Theseus, the great hero of Athens. By this action he saved his people from the terrible blood-toll they had long paid to the hardhearted Minos: seven young men and seven maidens who were brought from Athens every year to be devoured by the Minotaur. Daedalus helped Theseus to overcome the monster, and when the king learned of it his anger was terrible. Overnight, Daedalus found himself a prisoner in the very labyrinth he had created, along with Icarus, his son. Now, the two of them had but one thought in their heads: how to find their way out of the maze and flee from Crete.

"Slavery is hard to bear," said Daedalus, "but ten times

harder for an artist. Yet how can we leave Crete if we can't even find our way out of the labyrinth?"

"Only the birds are free," replied his son. "If we could fly like them, we could escape from here. But, alas, the gods did not give men wings."

"They gave them brains, though, Icarus," replied his father, then suddenly fell silent, wrapped in thought.

"Yes, we have brains," continued Icarus, "but if we had wings, too, how wonderful it would be! We would soar high into the sky, as high as the sun; we would travel like the birds, like the clouds, like the gods themselves!"

But Daedalus was no longer paying any attention to his son's words. He was looking fixedly up into the sky and thinking hard, for a bold idea had come into his head.

He was still sitting, wrapped in thought, when Minos' wife, Pasiphae, came to visit the two prisoners.

Pasiphae was not cast in the same cruel mould as her husband, and it grieved her greatly to see the great artist and his son locked up like common criminals. Knowing the loneliness of imprisonment, she would often come to the labyrinth to console them with her company and her conversation.

As soon as he saw the queen, Daedalus burst out:

"There are many things I can bear, but to see these hands lying idle, bound in slavery, that is more than I can endure!"

"Even if I could get you out of here," replied the queen, "you would be recaptured at once." And then she added:

"Today, news came from Athens that Theseus has been crowned king, and your banishment has been lifted."

"At last!" cried Daedalus in joy. "Now I can return to my homeland."

"No, Daedalus," replied the queen. "I told you escape was no easy matter, and from now on it will be even more difficult. When Minos learned that the people of Athens wish you to return he was overcome with rage. He ordered guards to be posted all over Crete, even though you are still safely locked up in the labyrinth. He is so afraid that you will get away that he is having the whole coastline watched, and the ports are being checked with such thoroughness that not even a needle could be slipped out undetected. I still want to help you, but I simply don't know how."

"By bringing us feathers," Daedalus answered. "As many feathers as you can lay your hands on. I want swansdown and eagles' quills, storks' pinions and the plumes from vultures' wings. Bring me feathers, and I shall make us wings of our own."

"But Daedalus, I never heard of such a thing," gasped the queen. "How do you know it will work?"

"Bring us the feathers I asked for, if you really want to help," was Daedalus' reply.

The queen was so impressed by the confidence and determination in his voice that she decided to do as she was asked. If anyone had the ingenuity and skill to carry off such a feat, it was Daedalus.

The very next day, Pasiphae began to supply them with feathers, careful to bring them in little by little, in quantities small enough to hide.

Daedalus set to work immediately. With great skill and artistry he fitted them all together, using wax to hold each feather in place. The work was delicate and needed both time and patience, but within a few days the wings had taken shape.

There were four of them, like a bird's wings in every respect, but very much larger, and so beautifully made that even the gods would have envied them.

Using leather straps, Daedalus fastened one pair onto Icarus' arms and shoulders, and then he put on his own.

The time to test the wings had come. Beating his arms up and down, Daedalus rose effortlessly into the air. Icarus did the same, and his wings, too, bore him upwards. All was ready!

Before they set off, Daedalus looked his son in the eyes and said:

"Icarus, my child, the journey we are about to make is not an easy one. We have a long way to go, but we shall reach our destination safely if we take care. We must not fly too low, in case the waves soak the feathers, but we must not soar too high, either, for then the sun may melt the wax which holds our wings together. We must travel slowly and steadily, like storks, and then we can be sure of a safe and pleasant flight."

"When shall we reach Athens, father?" asked the young

man.

"I do not know, my son," replied Daedalus. "I have thought long and hard about this, and I fear that we should not go there. I am afraid that if we do, Minos will declare war at once – not only to bring us back to Crete, but to punish Athens for harbouring us. We must not allow bloodshed and destruction to fall upon our city on our account."

"I shall be following you, father, and we shall go wherever you decide."

"That is how it must be, my son," replied Daedalus. "And now the great moment has come – a moment mankind may never forget. Follow me, and remember my advice." And with these words he lifted his great wings and soared into the sky with Icarus close behind.

Moments later they passed over the palace of king Minos, where the anxious Pasiphae had been watching on the great terrace since early morning. Just as they came over, Minos walked out in search of his wife and his eyes beheld a sight beyond belief.

"Pasiphae!" he cried. "Pasiphae! I have never seen such a thing. Two gods flying in the sky!"

"Gods indeed," replied Pasiphae and turned her face aside so that he should not see the tears which filled her eyes.

Daedalus and Icarus flew surely and steadily onwards. Soon they were looking down on the first of the Cyclades, an island shaped like a half moon. This was Thera, or all that was left of it after the great volcanic eruption which had engulfed the island's centre.

Flying northwards, they came to Naxos, the island of Dionysus, and then Delos, with its great temple of Apollo. At last, open sea stretched out beneath them once more.

Icarus was delighted with his new wings and swooped and soared as he flew. Harmless games enough they seemed, but Daedalus was worried, and cried out:

"Steady there, Icarus!"

"Don't worry, father," the boy shouted back, "there's no danger."

"There is, my boy, there is. Be careful. We're on a journey, not playing games!"

But unfortunately, Icarus thought he knew everything, and would not listen to his father's advice. That is how Phaethon came to a sad end, and that is how Icarus, too, was destined to die. So it has been for thousands of years, and so it will always be. Yet mankind needs courage, and youth cannot be blamed if it has more daring than its elders.

And Icarus was nothing if not daring. The higher he went, the more his spirits rose. The sun drew him like a magnet, and his father's warning flew right out of his mind.

When Daedalus next turned his head to check that all was well with Icarus, there was no sign of the boy. Close to panic, he scanned the skies from horizon to horizon, till finally he made out a tiny dot, rapidly approaching the sun's bright disc.

*...The sun melted the wax and the feathers were scattered
in the air...*

"Icarus!" he shouted despairingly. "Icarus, come back!"
But in spite of the urgency of Daedalus' voice, his words were
lost in the boundless expanses of the sky and never reached
his son's ears.

And soon the very thing happened which Daedalus had
feared. The sun melted the wax and the feathers were scattered in the air. Soon there was not a single feather left, and
Icarus fell like a stone from the heights. With frantic wingbeats,
Daedalus made a desperate effort to catch him, but it was all
in vain, and the daring young man found a watery grave in
the arms of the blue sea far below.

On labouring wings Daedalus carried the body of his son
to the nearest island, and there he buried him. Ever since, the
island has been called Icaria and the sea around it, the Icarian
sea, and all over the world the name of Icarus is remembered
whenever men wish to honour those who gave their lives to
make the dream of flight come true.

Shattered by the death of his son, Daedalus now had but
one wish: to put the greatest distance possible between himself and the place where the boy had fallen. And so he flew
westwards, on and on, until he reached Sicily.

When he at last made landfall, his first act was to destroy
the wings which had cost Icarus his life. Then he made his
way to the court of king Cocalus and offered his services in
return for royal protection.

Cocalus received Daedalus gladly and entrusted a number of important projects to him including, it is said, the mighty walls of Acragas in southern Sicily.

Meanwhile, Minos had not been sitting with folded hands. As soon as he learned of Daedalus' escape, he set out with a mighty fleet to find the master craftsman and bring him back to Crete.

Minos did not expect any help in his task. Wherever Daedalus had gone, the local people would want to keep him for themselves. And so the king of Crete employed a cunning trick. He did not reveal that he was searching for Daedalus, but took with him a conch shell, a gift from the sea god, Triton. This shell had a small hole at its pointed end, and, by blowing through it, Triton could raise storms and gales.

Everywhere he went, Minos would show people the shell and ask if anyone could pass a thread through its open mouth, round the spirals of the interior and out of the hole. And, of course, he promised a rich reward to the first man who could solve the problem.

Minos went all over the world without finding a single person who could pass a thread through the shell, until at last he came to Sicily and gave it to king Cocalus. He accepted the challenge and took the shell to Daedalus, and the cunning inventor, having smeared a little honey round the narrow opening at its tip, placed an ant in the broad lip of the shell, with a fine thread tied to its leg. Drawn by the sweet scent of the honey, the ant made its way down the spirals of the interior drawing the thread behind it till it reached the small hole at the other end. Bursting with pride, Cocalus bore the threaded shell back to king Minos.

As soon as he set eyes on it, Minos knew whose work this was. There was no one in the world could find the answer to such a problem except the man he had been searching for so long.

"This is the work of Daedalus!" he shouted joyfully. "Bring him here immediately, for he returns to Crete with me!"

Now Cocalus had no wish at all to deliver Daedalus into the hands of this Cretan tyrant, but on the other hand he had a healthy respect for Minos' evil temper and the huge army that lay on board his ships. He knew that if he dared refuse, the ruler of Crete would bring him and his kingdom to ruin.

And so he promised to release Daedalus, and meanwhile invited Minos to enjoy the hospitality of his palace. By now, all Sicily was up in arms, for not a man on the island wanted Daedalus to fall into the cruel king's hands.

"We would rather go down fighting than betray a man who sought our protection," they cried, "especially one who has done so many wonderful things for us."

When Cocalus saw their mood, he took his closest advisers aside to find some means of ridding themselves of Minos. And in the end they found a way. While he was taking a bath, they poured two cauldrons of boiling water on his body, scalding him to death. And so the Cretan forces would not attack, they claimed it had all been an accident.

Such was the inglorious end of the feared and mighty king of Crete.

Yet after his death Minos became one of the judges of the shades in Hades, as we saw in an earlier book. He may have been cruel and unjust on earth but he was, after all, a son of Zeus and mankind had to learn to bow to the will of the gods, just or unjust as it might be.

After Minos died, Daedalus returned at last to Athens where he spent the rest of his days, working and teaching true art to younger men to the very last. Towards the end of his life, he founded the school which bore his name. It survived for hundreds of years and the many great artists that it bred were all called Daedalides.

PELOPS AND OENOMAUS

Whoever goes to Olympia today and visits its museum will certainly stand in awe before the statues which once adorned the two pediments of the temple of Zeus. The one which decorated the eastern end shows the chariot race between Pelops and Oenomaus, while the western one depicts the battle between the Centaurs and the Lapiths.

If only because they are portrayed in such great works of art, these two myths deserve to be retold.

But before we begin the myth of Oenomaus and Pelops, we must tell the story of the latter's father, Tantalus.

In Phrygia, in Asia Minor, beneath the sacred mountain Tmolus, where Midas had once been king, Tantalus, son of Zeus by the oceanid Pluto, was now upon the throne.

Tantalus had all that a ruler could wish for. His ploughlands were fertile and gave bountiful crops. His lush meadows were filled with grazing flocks led by curly-horned rams, while riders on proud horses drove great herds of cattle to other pastures. Every day, rich gifts reached the court of Tantalus, the offerings of chiefs who acknowledged his dominion. And besides all this wealth he had the gold washed down from the mountains by the Pactolus, the richest gold-bearing river in the world.

As if all this were not enough, Tantalus enjoyed a closer friendship with the gods than any other man on earth. They would often come from Olympus to eat, drink and make merry with him in his golden palaces, and at other times they would invite him to their symposia on Olympus to drink nectar and ambrosia with the gods.

Zeus was so fond of his son that he would even ask him to attend their councils and join with the Olympians in taking those great decisions which determined the fate of mankind.

But the love shown to him by Zeus and the other gods filled Tantalus with such pride that he began to consider himself their superior. Little by little, his respect for them diminished. He began to take nectar and ambrosia from Olympus to toast his friends on earth, and he revealed the secrets of the gods to mortal men to show the world what a splendid fellow he was. Zeus warned him that if he wished to keep his friendship with the Olympians he must be more careful, but Tantalus replied in an insolent and haughty tone:

"I shall do whatever I please. I am a mighty ruler in my own right, and accept advice from no one."

Zeus frowned his disapproval, but he loved his son so much that he let his pride go unpunished.

The only result of this was an even worse act of impiety on Tantalus' part: he swore a false oath to the gods, solemnly declaring he had no idea what had become of Laelaps, their beloved golden dog of Crete, whereas the truth was that he not only knew the whereabouts of their favourite animal, but had hidden it himself!

Until that moment, no god had ever lied on oath, and every mortal who had done so had paid the penalty. Zeus was enraged when he heard what his son had done. Yet once again his fatherly love overcame his harsher feelings and Tantalus went unpunished.

Instead of being grateful for the mercy Zeus had shown him, Tantalus took the gods' inaction for a sign of weakness. Blinded by his high opinion of himself, he came to believe that the only real proof of power was to commit the most hideous crime imaginable without suffering any of its evil consequences.

Once this sick belief had planted itself in his head, Tantalus began to rack his brain for the cruellest and most horrible act a man could dream of. And, unfortunately, he was not long in finding it: he decided to butcher his own son and serve him up to the gods at a banquet. His aim was not only to humiliate them, but to show the world that the Olympians were not the all-knowing creatures they liked mankind to think them, if they could not even tell what they were eating!

So Tantalus invited the gods to his palace and served them the vilest meal the world had ever known.

But there was no deceiving the immortals: they knew at once what had been set before them and refused to touch the meat. Now, all eyes turned on Zeus. The countenance of the ruler of gods and men had blackened with fearsome rage. Thunder and lightning shook the earth. A crime such as this could never go unpunished and, with a look of loathing, Zeus hurled his son into the dark kingdom of Hades to suffer eternal torture.

Tantalus was condemned to stand in a pool of crystal-clear water. He was soon afflicted by thirst and wished to drink, but as soon as he leaned forward to do so the water disappeared, leaving only parched, dry earth where it had been. Immediately he returned to an upright position, the water came flooding back waist-high. Again and again Tantalus tried to quench his thirst, but he could not even catch a single drop to wet his cracked and burning lips. He was condemned to the torture of eternal thirst. But this was not all. Over his head hung branches laden with ripe and luscious fruit, and Tantalus was torn by the most terrible pangs of hunger. He stretched up a hand to pluck a fruit and ease the pain which clutched at his entrails, but as he did so the branches rose beyond his grasp. Time and again he reached upwards, but each time he reached in vain. He was condemned to the torture of eternal hunger. And as if these unbearable punishments were not enough, a third was added to them: a huge rock hung teetering above Tantalus' head, threatening to fall at any moment and crush him beneath its weight. Every time it swayed or creaked, Tantalus was seized with terror. Yet the rock never fell upon him, and so he was condemned to the torture of eternal fear.

When Zeus saw that the miserable king of Phrygia was well punished for his horrible deed, he called Hermes and ordered him to gather up all the pieces of Tantalus' son from the table, to wash them well and then to fit together once again the young man who had been so cruelly slaughtered. Hermes obeyed his father's orders with great care and skill, but when he had finished there was a piece still missing from the shoulder. It had been eaten by Demeter, who had lost her daughter, Persephone, and was too upset to realize what was on her plate. However, Hephaestus replaced the missing part with cunningly worked ivory and finally Zeus breathed life into the body. The young man who had been saved was named Pelops, and he would always have an ivory patch on his shoulder. For that reason they still say that anyone who has a white mark on any part of the body is a descendant of his.

Pelops succeeded to his father's throne, but he did not rule for long. He was defeated in battle by Ilus, King of Troy, and obliged to flee his kingdom.

With him he took his sister, Niobe, of whom we shall tell in the next book, and as much of his father's gold as he could carry. Then, together with a few faithful friends, he made his way westwards into Greece.

His wanderings finally brought him to Pisa, a city near Olympia ruled by king Oenomaus.

Oenomaus had a beautiful daughter, Hippodameia, but he did not wish to find a husband for her because the oracle had warned him that he was destined to be killed by the man she married. To forestall this fate, Oenomaus decided to kill every man who asked him for her hand, and he warned all prospective suitors that he would only give away his daughter if one of them could beat him in a chariot race. Whoever lost would die on the end of Oenomaus' lance.

The contest was one-sided: the king was always as sure of victory as his opponents were of death, for his horses were swifter than the wild north wind and he was the finest charioteer in the whole of Greece.

In spite of this, Hippodameia's beauty had already drawn thirteen suitors to accept the challenge and pit their skills against the king of Pisa. All of them had been defeated and had met their end at the point of his cruel lance.

And now Pelops decided to face Oenomaus, for he, too, had fallen under the spell of Hippodameia's charms.

Hippodameia loved Pelops and she begged him not to add his name to the long list of fallen heroes.

"His horses are the swiftest in the world and there is not a charioteer in Greece can match him. I would rather you went away and never saw me again than learn that you had sacrificed your life for me."

"I shall not lose my life," replied Pelops, "but Oenomaus will lose a daughter. My horses were a gift from Poseidon himself and they are as swift as the wind. The gods are on my side, and they will help me to win."

And so Pelops appeared before Oenomaus, asked his daughter's hand in marriage and declared himself ready for the chariot race.

"Very well," was the king's answer. "Since you place no value on your young life, then neither shall I. I shall do you the same favour I have always done the others and let you set off an hour before me, but as soon as my chariot overtakes yours, I shall kill you."

Pelops, however, had Hermes on his side.

"Are we going to let him die now, when we went to so much trouble to undo his father's murderous work?" he asked.

Exactly the same thought had been running through Zeus' mind, so with his father's blessing Hermes hastened to find his son Myrtilus, who was the king of Pisa's chief charioteer.

"Listen, Myrtilus," said Hermes. "This time I want Oenomaus to be killed and not his opponent. I want you to see to it

that something goes wrong with your master's chariot during the race."

Now Myrtilus lacked none of his wily father's cunning, and it did not take him long to work out what to do.

That night, he went to Oenomaus' chariot, took out the locking pin which held the off-side wheel to the axle and replaced it with another, made of wax.

The contest was to begin next morning. They would set off from the temple of Zeus at Olympia and race eastwards for the Isthmus of Corinth, in an attempt to reach the temple of Poseidon there by dusk.

As usual, Oenomaus gave his opponent an hour's start while

he went to sacrifice to Zeus. By the time the sacrifice had
been made Pelops was well ahead, but Oenomaus jumped
into his chariot and shot off like a bolt of lightning. However,
Tantalus' son had swift horses too and so the king of Pisa
rode on for some hours without seeing any sign of him.
Oenomaus began to feel anxious and whipped his horses up
to a faster pace. It was the first time he had come so far without overtaking his opponent. Finally he made out Pelops'
chariot way ahead in the distance. The sight gave Oenomaus
renewed confidence and his horses surged forward as if filled
with new strength. The gap between them narrowed steadily.
Pelops turned his head and saw the fearsome Oenomaus ad-

vancing on him like a storm-front. A desperate race began.
Pelops' horses thundered wildly forwards, as if they knew
some dreadful enemy was descending upon them. Oenomaus
strained to close the distance, but with a superhuman effort
Pelops urged his horses into an even faster gallop. The two
opponents sped onwards, their hearts in their mouths, knowing only too well that this was a race between life and death.
Oenomaus made another great effort, lashing his horses furiously, and little by little he began to gain ground. Pelops'
horses could go no faster and the gap was closing quicker.
Nothing could hold Oenomaus now. His feet beat a frenzied
rhythm on the chariot floor and his deadly javelin quivered in
his hand. A savage joy shone in his face as he saw the moment of victory and death draw near. The end of the race was
in sight: away in the distance, the temple of Poseidon could
just be made out. Oenomaus came on faster still. Pelops struggled hopelessly to pull ahead, but his horses had given the
last ounce of their strength. "O, gods!" he cried. "Why abandon me now, when you saved me from my father's wrath!"
But it seemed that the gods had indeed forgotten him, for the
wax pin still held as firm as iron and Oenomaus surged forward like a hurricane, his wheels beating a wild tattoo on the
stony track. The moment he was waiting for had come. With
a hair-raising cry he flexed his arm to plunge his deadly lance
in Pelops' back, when suddenly his right wheel flew into the
air, the royal chariot overturned and Oenomaus was dragged

headlong over the stones to a horrible death.

That was the end of the bloodthirsty king of Pisa, and that, too, was the end of the race. Thanks to Myrtilus, Pelops was declared the victor, married the lovely Hippodameia and became the ruler of Oenomaus' kingdom.

But as you will have noticed, there are few happy endings in the stories we have to tell. For all their magical inventiveness, myths are not fairy tales where "they all lived happily ever after," and the story of Pelops is no exception to the rule.

When he learned it was Hermes himself who had saved him, the new king of Pisa built a temple in his honour, the first that had ever been raised in the god's name in the whole world. He also summoned Myrtilus to receive his reward.

"Ask me for whatever you wish, and I shall give it to you," Pelops announced, without asking himself what Myrtilus might now demand. And it was an unwelcome answer that Hermes' son had ready for him: he wanted half Pelops' new kingdom, neither more nor less.

The thought of handing over such a prize was a painful one. All night long Pelops dwelt on it, and in the morning he went in search of Myrtilus and took him out into the country on the pretext of pacing out the boundaries of the young charioteer's share of the land. But instead of this, he led him to the summit of a high cliff and with a sudden push sent him tumbling into the foaming seas below.

As he fell to his death, Myrtilus laid a curse on Pelops and all his descendants. The son of Tantalus begged Hermes to protect him from the evil spell, but though the god had saved him twice before, this time Pelops begged in vain. Hermes turned a deaf ear, for he had killed not only his son but the man who had helped to save his life. Myrtilus' curse took hold: Pelops, his children and his children's children suffered great misfortunes, committed foul crimes and were punished harshly by the gods. Yet for all this the name of Pelops was not forgotten. The land to which he had come was given his name, and has been known as the Peloponnese ever since.

This is the tragic story told in marble on the eastern pediment of the temple of Zeus at Olympia. The other brings the tale of the Lapiths and the Centaurs to life.

The Lapiths were a race who lived in Thessaly. One of their kings was Ixion, whom we have spoken of in an earlier book. There, we also learned how the first Centaur was born. Most people say the Centaurs were the descendants of Ixion and Nephele. They were strange creatures, half horse and half man, and wild, too, with a few exceptions such as the wise Centaur Cheiron who was also immortal. Many mythical figures came to him to be taught, even gods, like Asclepius, who learned medicine at his side.

The Centaurs were neighbours of the Lapiths. They lived on Mount Pelion, and, until the time of this story, there had been no quarrels between them.

The king of the Lapiths was now the hero Peirithous. He was about to celebrate his wedding to the lovely Deidameia and had announced a great feast, with heroes from all over Greece as his guests. As the Centaurs were descended from a Lapith king he invited them to the celebrations, too, along with their leader, Eurytion, and offered them hospitality in a cave near his palace.

Peirithous' servants set tables in the cave and loaded them with rich food and great flagons of strong wine. The centaurs, however, not knowing such liquor should be mixed with water, swallowed it neat and were soon roaring drunk.

In his cups, Eurytion was seized by an irresistible urge. With a clatter of hooves he galloped out of the cave, burst into the great banqueting hall of the palace and tried to seize Peirithous' lovely bride.

Livid with rage at this insult, which showed no more respect for him than for his bride, Peirithous drew his sword and launched himself at Eurytion. The other guests followed suit, and the leader of the Centaurs fled back to the cave, his face streaming blood.

"Look what Peirithous has done to me!" he cried. "Come on, let's go back and carry off their wives!"

These words were all the excuse the drunken Centaurs needed to storm into the palace and throw themselves on the Lapith women.

The Lapiths drew their swords once more, and a savage

battle now began. The Centaurs armed themselves with chairs and tripods, broken table legs and whatever else in the palace they could lay their hands on. Soon the walls echoed with the dreadful din of their fighting. The Lapiths defended their women with great heroism, but even so, some of the Centaurs managed to snatch up Lapith girls and carry them off, at which the others galloped out after them. Peirithous came running in pursuit, his countrymen and the other heroes close behind, and the battle was resumed in the open air as fiercely as before. The Centaurs used their immense strength to heave huge boulders at the heroes and beat at them with wooden clubs, but at the critical moment Peirithous' good friend Theseus, the mighty hero of Athens, came to the Lapiths' aid. Eurytion was the first to fall beneath his blows, and at this the Lapiths took courage, and, led by the Athenian champion, they fell on the Centaurs with renewed strength.

The battle became a bloodbath and only a handful of Centaurs managed to escape by fleeing to the mountains. But not even these lived long. Within a few years they all met their deaths, pierced by the deadly arrows of Heracles, whom they had tried to kill.

And so the forests and the mountains were freed from the wild and savage Centaurs. Not even Cheiron escaped, though Heracles had not wished to harm him. Mortally wounded by a stray arrow, yet still immortal, the wise Centaur suffered all the pangs of death for many years, until he could endure no longer and begged Zeus to let him die and so release him from eternal agony.

EUROPA AND CADMUS

In those distant days, there reigned in the East, in fabled Sidon, a king named Agenor, son of the earth-shaker Poseidon and the Oceanid Libya.

Agenor had three sons: Phoenix, Cilix and Cadmus, and a daughter, Europa, who was so lovely that even the goddess Aphrodite was envious of her beauty.

One night, Europa dreamed that two women were struggling bitterly for her possession. One was called the East and the other the West. If the East won, Europa would remain in her birthplace among her own people, but if the West were the victor, then she would leave with her on a long voyage beyond the blue sea to the regions where the sun sets in majesty each night.

It was the West who won that struggle. Torn with grief, the East was obliged to bid farewell to the lovely princess her soil had borne and raised, and whose dazzling beauty was the pride of all Asia.

Europa woke in terror, for nothing in the world would induce her to leave the land that had given her birth and the parents she loved so deeply. Kneeling in prayer, she begged the gods, and above all Zeus, to save her from exile and the loss of her dear ones.

But Zeus had other plans for the girl. It was he who had sent the god of dreams to trouble her sleep, for he had wished her to come willingly to the West, and he was far from pleased when he saw that Europa shuddered at the very thought of leaving home. Be that as it may, mighty Zeus was stirred by the desire to bring the lovely princess to Greece and make her his wife, and what Zeus wished had to be accomplished. Now that Oneiros, god of dreams, had failed him he contrived a secret plan to carry off the unsuspecting maiden.

One sunny spring day, Europa and her friends went out with baskets to gather flowers and enjoy the beauty of the countryside. Dancing and skipping for joy, they came to a flowery meadow and soon made it echo with their happy cries and songs. Before them stretched the boundless sea, calm and inviting, while in a green field nearby the herds of Europa's father, king Agenor, stood grazing.

The princess laughed and played with her friends, running from flower to flower as happily as a lark. She wore a charming red dress and her face was radiant with the delight of sharing such surroundings with companions she loved. The breeze caressed her silken hair and the golden rays of the sun bathed it in their glory, making her lovely face more beautiful still.

As they were playing, a handsome white bull ambled away from Agenor's herd and slowly made its way towards Europa. The splendid beast drew the princess' attention like a magnet, gazing at her with its great, expressive eyes as if in admiration. And all the while it drew gradually closer, gambolling playfully as if it were seeking her company.

It was an animal of astonishing beauty. Its snowy-white hide, unusual in a bull, gave it an air of added majesty. A black band on its forehead set off its white head to perfection, while its widespread horns, shining like two half moons of precious stone, were the crowning glory of this superb creature. And on its breath there was the sweet smell of ambrosia.

But it was not only the beauty and the noble appearance of the bull which captured Europa's attention. It was also so clearly friendly. In fact, it seemed so gentle and harmless that

Europa did not hesitate to walk towards it in her turn and caress its massive neck. And then she called out to her friends to come and admire the magnificent animal. Not even in the herds of the gods could there be another creature like this!

Europa and the bull were soon firm friends. Taking great care not to harm her, the gentle animal played with the lovely princess and finally went down on its knees, inviting her to climb up and ride. Without hesitation, Europa gaily mounted its broad, velvety back. Delighted, the bull began to play again, trotting in and out among Europa's laughing companions. With light and gambolling steps it made its way towards the sea, with Europa waving her hand and her friends responding with a laughing mock farewell. But this farewell, intended in jest, was soon to prove all too real. For a moment later the bull quickened its pace and drew away from the group of girls. Europa was now becoming anxious and wanted to get down, but this was no longer possible, for the bull had broken into a gallop, and seconds later it charged into the sea. Terror-stricken, the lovely maiden clung to the beast's horns and cried out desperately for help. But it was already too late: swimming with speed and grace the bull drew further and further away from the shore, bearing on its back the princess it had so cunningly carried off. For the bull was none other than Zeus himself, who had wrought this transformation to deceive the lovely daughter of Agenor and spirit her away to the land of the setting sun.

*...With light and gambolling steps it made its way
towards the sea...*

Their progress to the West was stately and triumphant. Poseidon, the brother of Zeus, who rules over the sea, cast down his magic trident on the waves, commanding the waters to be still and not wet so much as the hem of Europa's dress. With his wife Amphitrite at his side, he rode behind the bull Zeus and Europa in a golden chariot drawn by four prancing sea horses. A host of nereids followed in the sea god's wake, while on both sides dolphins plunged and jumped in joy and seabirds wheeled overhead. And heading the procession went his son, young Triton, blowing triumphant peals on a great conch horn to herald the coming of Agenor's daughter to the West.

But she, poor girl, knew nothing of what all this meant and clung in fear to the bull's back, remembering with longing her home and her dear ones and wondering whether she would ever see them again.

And in this way they arrived in Crete.

Ever since that day, Crete and Greece and the whole of the continent which lies to the West, as far as the great ocean, have borne the name of Europa, the lovely maiden who came from the East against her will.

In the cave of Dicte, hidden high among the Cretan mountains, the Four Seasons made ready the bridal bed for Zeus' beloved. The Three Graces sprinkled the fragrance of beauty upon her and combed her silken hair until there was no woman in the world could rival the loveliness of Europa.

When all was ready, Zeus, now transformed into an eagle, was united with her at last. From this sacred union were born three sons: Minos, the fabled ruler of Crete, Rhadamanthys, the wise law-maker, and Sarpedon, the first king of Lycia.

Zeus presented Europa with many rich gifts. Among them were Laelaps, a hunting dog which never let its prey escape and a golden bow with magic arrows which always hit their mark.

But Zeus' constant fear was that Europa might leave Crete or be found by her father Agenor and taken back to the East. To guard against such a possibility he set the terrible giant Talos to keep watch over the island.

Talos was no ordinary giant. He had neither mother nor father, but was the creation of Hephaestus, master-craftsman of the gods, who had forged him from solid bronze and then breathed life and fearsome strength into his body. Talos was invincible: neither arrow, spear nor sword could pierce his brazen flanks. And he was not only invincible but immortal. For magic blood which gave him everlasting life coursed through his frame in veins of bronze. Hephaestus had sealed it inside his body with a golden plug set in his right foot.

Talos mounted guard over Crete both night and day, patrolling the island watchfully and shaking the regions he passed through with the thud of his heavy footsteps. No foreign ship would approach the great island for fear that the terrible giant might hurl a mighty rock and sink it in an instant.

Talos' awe-inspiring strength served as protection not only for Zeus' beloved, the fair Europa, but for the whole of Crete. Wealthy though the island might be, no would-be conqueror even dared think of setting foot on it.

Talos, of course, was a figment of men's imagination. But even so this myth, like many others, holds a grain of truth. It is indeed true that Crete feared no invader in those days; the island empire was so mighty that its cities had neither walls nor fortresses to guard them. While the story may have had it that the fearsome giant Talos guarded the island, it was a giant of another, but equally impressive kind which really performed that task: the Cretan people and their powerful fleet. And when, with the passing of time, the power of Crete began to wane, so the myth took shape. It is said that Talos was killed by the Argonauts, or rather by their leader, Jason, with the help of his wife, Medea. She made the giant tipsy with wine and Jason pulled out the golden plug which held the magic blood in his veins. It came gushing out and Talos became a lifeless statue of bronze; and ever afterwards, all those who looked on it remembered the lost majesty of Crete and were silent.

But the myth of Europa has another chapter.

When king Agenor learned that his daughter had been carried off, he was almost beside himself with grief and determined to do whatever lay in his power to find the girl and bring her back. So he called his three sons, Phoenix, Cilix and Cadmus and told them:

"Listen to what I command. The anguish I feel for my beloved daughter is more than my heart can bear. Only if she is found again shall I find peace. You are young and strong. Go, and search everywhere. Scour the whole world until you find Europa and bring her back to me. But do not dare to return without your sister – for if you come back empty-handed I shall give you cause to regret it."

And so Agenor's three sons took their most devoted servants and went in search of Europa, each one taking a different road.

Phoenix set off towards the south, but it was a blind and fruitless search and he soon lost hope and abandoned the effort. Because he was afraid to return to his father without Europa, he stayed where his wanderings had brought him and ruled over a land which ever since has been called Phoenicia.

The same future lay in store for Cilix, who had struck out northwards. He too remained and became king of the country which took his name: Cilicia.

But Agenor's youngest son was of a far different mettle from his brothers. For him, a father's command was a sacred bond. Cadmus had a strength and courage not given to common men, and he was determined to achieve the impossible if by so doing his sister could be reunited with her family. Yet how was he to know that Zeus himself was keeping Europa hidden away, and that all his efforts were thus doomed to failure from the start?

Cadmus and his little band of faithful followers boarded a ship and set off towards the West. They had been sailing for some days when they finally made out the mountains of Crete in the distance.

"We must go ashore here and begin our search," said Cadmus.

"We cannot even approach this island," was the captain's reply. "A fearsome giant guards it by night and day. As soon as he sets eyes on a foreign ship he throws half a mountainside at it and smashes it to driftwood and by the same reasoning, I don't see how Europa could have landed on Crete. No, it is elsewhere that our search must begin."

And so they left behind them the island where, had they but known it, Europa lay concealed and continued their voyage until they made landfall in Greece.

There, Cadmus went from city to city asking after his sister, but he heard not a single word that might lead to her whereabouts until somebody told him:

"Only Pythia the seer can tell you where Europa is hidden. Go to the Oracle of Apollo at Delphi, and if you learn nothing there, then you must resign yourself to the fact that you will never see her again."

A few days later Cadmus reached Delphi and asked where

and how he could find his sister.

The answer the oracle gave him was as follows:

"Son of Agenor, give up your vain search for Europa, for you will never find her anywhere. But in the morning, as soon as rosy-fingered Dawn appears in the heavens, go instead and seek the cattle of king Pelagon. There in his herd you will find a cow marked with the sign of the moon on each flank. Let that beast be your guide, and when it is weary from its wanderings and sinks to the ground, then offer it in sacrifice to Mother Earth and sprinkle its blood on the soil of your new homeland. For in that place you will build a mighty fortress which you will call Cadmea, and at its feet a city with wide streets which shall be named Thebes."

When Cadmus received this reply he realized that it was the will of the gods that he should never find Europa and so next morning at daybreak he set out in search of the animal Pythia had told him of. It did not take him long to find the herd of king Pelagon, and among the cows there stood out one with a moon-shaped mark on each flank. As if it knew what it must do, the beast began to walk away, and Cadmus followed it. The animal made its way eastwards, crossing the whole province of Phocis without stopping to rest, and then made its way into the region named Boeotia where it finally lay down on the grass, exhausted.

Then Cadmus thanked Apollo for the help his oracle had given, kissed the soil of his new homeland, and together with

his followers built an altar to sacrifice the sacred beast to
Mother Earth. But there was no water for the sacrifice, and so
he sent his servants in search of some.

His men soon found a spring in a cave and began to fill
their flasks. But suddenly a huge and hideous dragon darted
out of a cleft in the rock, plunged its ugly head into their
midst and tore them all to pieces.

Cadmus awaited their return in vain. Eventually, following their tracks, he reached the cave – and found his companions lying dead.

At that very moment a blood-curdling hiss made him spin
round and he beheld the fearsome dragon rearing its head to
strike.

Like lightning, Cadmus seized a huge rock and hurled it at
the beast, but the dragon's scales were harder than stone and
the blow left it unharmed. However, this setback did not dis-
courage Agenor's son for a single instant. Seizing his spear,
he drove it between the scales and into the monster's spine.
And then all hell broke loose. The hideous creature writhed
in agony, hurling itself upon the rocks and scattering them far
and wide. It thrashed the trees with its tail, snapping them
like dry twigs. Cadmus sprang from one side to the other to
avoid the rears and plunges of the dragon, till finally the opportunity he sought presented itself and he thrust his sword
with awesome strength through the raging beast's throat, pin-
ning it to a huge old oak tree. For all its massive trunk and

...Finally the opportunity Cadmus sought presented itself...

towering height the tree crashed to the ground as the monster
writhed in its death struggles, but Cadmus jumped nimbly
aside and escaped unharmed. Suddenly, all was still. The fearful dragon was dead at last.

The brave young man could not believe his eyes when he
saw what an awesome beast he had slain. He stood in wonder
for a while, then finally took water and went to carry out the
sacrifice alone. When it was done, he lifted his arms towards
the sky and cried:

"I cannot tell, but surely some god lent me the strength to
kill this monster, for no man could have done a deed like this
unaided. To that unknown god I give thanks from the depths
of my heart."

Hardly were these words out of his mouth when Athena,
goddess of wisdom, appeared before him.

"The gods help those who help themselves," the blue-eyed
goddess told him. "This great feat was yours alone. Only, be
warned that this dragon was a son of Ares, god of war, and
perhaps a day will come when he will make you pay for the
killing, justified though it was. But now, listen closely. Go
and pull out the dragon's teeth, one by one, and sow them in
the earth. Do what I tell you without delay, and do not ask me
why."

As soon as she had said these words, the goddess disappeared.

Cadmus had no idea why he should perform such a pointless task, yet he did as the goddess had commanded. However, he had hardly finished sowing the dragon's teeth when some strange gleaming shoots began to appear in the soil which he had planted. It soon became clear that these shoots were none other than the tips of war lances slowly pushing their way out of the ground. Before long, the crests of helmets appeared beside the spears, then the heads of warriors, and finally, fully-armed fighting men emerged whole from the earth, shields on their arms and swords at their sides.

At the sight of this new foe which had sprung up before his eyes Cadmus made as if to draw his sword, but his hand was not half way to the sheath when one of the warriors cried out:

"Leave your sword in its place, son of Agenor. Others will fight for you."

And with these words a savage battle broke out among the earth-sprung warriors. Swords and lances clashed furiously, and one by one the warriors fell dead upon the very soil which had so recently given them birth.

Only five men survived that murderous struggle, and they were the most valiant of them all. Giving their hands in friendship they bowed the knee to Cadmus and swore eternal loyalty and devotion to him. These were the Spartoe, which means in Greek 'the sown men', and they received their name because they had sprung from the dragon's teeth which Cadmus had planted.

With the help of the Spartoe the son of Agenor built the fortress of Cadmea, and beneath it he founded Thebes, the city which has borne this name ever since.

Cadmus proved a wise and popular king. He taught his people to love the fine arts and he gave them their first alphabet, which they called 'Cadmean' after the king who taught it.

He governed and administered his kingdom well, making just laws and reigning in peace, with neither wars nor conquests. This peace, and the well-being of his people, were safeguarded by a powerful army led by the valiant Spartoe, who had sprung from the dragon's teeth.

Cadmus married the lovely Harmonia, daughter of Aphrodite, goddess of beauty and love, and their wedding was an unforgettable occasion, graced by the presence and the rich gifts of all the gods. It is said that on the very spot where the market place of Thebes was later built, the thrones of the Olympians had been placed for the wedding ceremony. Apollo himself honoured the bridal couple with the music of his lyre. And even today men point out the spot where the Muses sang their timeless song, 'Love what is fair, but never what is foul.'

Only two immortals were absent from the wedding: Ares, god of war, because Cadmus had slain his son, the dragon; and Eris, goddess of strife, because she could not bear the company of those who truly loved one another.

For it was not so much the splendour of the wedding that

was memorable as the fact that in that moment gods and men united to join a couple who were themselves united by one of the greatest loves the world had ever seen.

Cadmus and Harmonia lived and reigned in joy and loving tenderness for many years, a model not only to Thebes but to the whole of Greece of what a marriage should be.

'May you always be as loving as Cadmus and Harmonia' was the wish on the lips of relatives and friends whenever a young couple got married in those times.

Yet if the love of Cadmus and Harmonia endured to the end, their happiness did not, for two of the four beloved daughters that were born to them, Semele and Ino, fell prey to the jealousy of the goddess Hera, and it cost them their lives.

Cadmus believed that these tragic deaths were somehow linked with Ares, who had never forgiven him for killing the dragon.

And so he handed the throne of Thebes to his grandson Pentheus and set out with Harmonia for the far north, lest other misfortunes fall upon his descendants. But even in exile nothing but pain and bitterness awaited them, for there news came that their other grandson, Actaeon, had fallen a tragic victim to the wrath of the goddess Artemis, and all through no fault of his own.

Bitterly grieved to see how the gods had turned against him, Cadmus now remembered the words of Athena on the day he had slain the dragon: "Perhaps a day will come when you will pay for the killing, justified though it was."

"If this is the price I must pay for slaying Ares' dragon," he cried, "then I would rather be turned into such a creature myself than see my children and my children's children so cruelly punished!"

He had not even finished speaking when he felt his body growing thin and long and saw scales forming over his skin. His head became narrow and wedge-shaped, his tongue split in two and his manly voice shrank to a hiss. Cadmus had become a serpent!

In her despair and loneliness, Harmonia begged the gods to turn her into a snake as well, rather than be separated from her husband. And this they did.

And so the honour, the glory and the joy of their prime were matched by an old age filled with misery and pain. Transformed into two harmless snakes, Cadmus and Harmonia dragged their weary way among the rocks and stones. The couple who had once been the darlings of the gods were now despised by mortal and immortal alike. The son of Agenor and the daughter of Aphrodite, who had known such love and given it so generously, who had helped so many and never harmed a fly, were forced at last to drink the bitter dregs of sorrow and despair – and no one could tell the reason why. Only in death did the gods take pity on them, for their souls did not descend into the dark depths of Hades but travelled to the Fortunate Isles, where there is neither anguish nor regret.

Years went by and a man came northwards on a quest. His name was Illyrius and he was the youngest son of Cadmus and Harmonia, the child of their old age. Drawn by his love for his parents he had set out in search of their grave, but finding nothing he stayed and ruled in the land where they had died. And the country has been called Illyria ever since.

ZETHUS AND AMPHION,
SONS OF ZEUS

Although Cadmus founded Thebes and built the fortress of Cadmea, it was two of his descendants, the twin brothers Zethus and Amphion, who built its fabled walls with their seven great gates.

The story of these two men and their mother, Antiope, is a strange and dramatic one.

Antiope was the daughter of Nycteus, king of Thebes, and such was her beauty that Zeus himself fell in love with her.

Their union produced two sons, Zethus and Amphion, and their gripping tale begins before they were even born.

As soon as she felt the children stirring in her womb, Antiope trembled at the thought of her father's wrath. Always a daunting figure, anger made him a man to quail before.

So hard-hearted was Nycteus that not long before he had refused to give Antiope in marriage to Epopeus, the young king of Sicyon, simply because he wanted to keep his daughter to comfort his old age! What could Antiope tell him now – that the father of her children was Zeus himself? It was easy enough to say, but would he believe her, or would he kill her? And even if he did not kill her, would she not be disgraced for ever?

"Epopeus is the only person I can tell," said Antiope to herself. "He will understand and offer me protection."

And so Antiope stole out of her father's home secretly in the night and after a long and tiring journey she arrived in Sicyon.

Epopeus received her joyfully and married her at once. Now, Antiope could give birth to her children without fearing anybody.

But the young couple had hardly got over their joy at being reunited when a messenger came running into the palace gasping:

"It's the Theban army, with Nycteus at their head, and his

brother Lycus. They've crossed the Isthmus of Corinth and they're headed here, for Sicyon!"

Epopeus immediately readied himself to face the king of Thebes. Antiope tried in vain to hold him back, begging him to hand her over to Nycteus instead.

"I would rather be taken from you, yet know you live, than mourn your death, my beloved!" she cried.

Ignoring Antiope's pleas, Epopeus challenged her cruel father to single combat. And both of them were slain. Then Lycus led the Theban troops into the city, carried off Antiope and returned to Thebes to become king.

But the new queen, Dirce, was an evil woman and her heart was filled with hatred for Antiope.

"Listen, Lycus," she warned her husband, "nobody must learn Antiope is with child, for if the truth be known, we shall never be sure that Thebes is safely in our grasp."

"Then what do you propose?" enquired the king.

"Hand her over to me," was the wicked queen's reply. "I know how to deal with her!"

Dirce locked Antiope in a gloomy dungeon, and within its dank walls the young woman gave birth to Zethus and Amphion, the sons of Zeus.

As soon as Dirce learned that the children had been born she snatched them cruelly from their mother, shut them in a basket and called the king's most trusty servant.

"Take these brats," she ordered, "climb Mount Cithaeron,

and leave them on the bleakest, most deserted slope you find. I'm not asking you to kill them – let the gods decide whether they should live or not. I want no charge of murder laid at my door."

These words were sheer hypocrisy, of course. For Dirce was perfectly sure that once the babies were exposed on the mountainside it would not be long before they died or were eaten by wolves.

Having dealt with the infants, Dirce then ordered another servant to shackle Antiope in heavy chains and double bar the door of her cell so she would never be able to escape.

Yet Zeus could not abandon his children, and so, carefully though Dirce had chosen her servant for that task, the lord of the gods poured the spirit of mercy and justice into the man's soul. His eyes were opened to the cruelty of his mistress and he was overcome with pity for Antiope's defenceless babies. High on the slopes of Cithaeron he found a kind shepherd and confessed to him that he had been ordered by queen Dirce to leave the children to die, on the mountainside. When he heard these words, the shepherd felt so sorry for the young things that he willingly agreed to take them and bring them up as his own children.

"Now my mind is at rest," said the servant, "for I am sure that I have left these helpless creatures in the hands of a kind and honest man. Know that their mother is Antiope, daughter of king Nycteus and wife of king Epopeus of Sicyon, who killed each other in single combat."

"But where is Antiope now?" asked the shepherd.

"I should not tell you this," replied the servant, "for though I have seen many injustices and held my tongue, this last was more than I could bear. Antiope is locked in an underground dungeon and not even allowed to see the light of day, though she has done nothing to deserve such a fate. But the worst of it is this: her children were torn from her arms and she believes that they are lost for ever now. I beg you, good shepherd, for my sake: keep my secret. Everything I have told you must remain between the two of us. Promise me that the children will never learn who their mother was."

When the servant had been given the promise he sought, he returned to Thebes and told the queen that her orders had been carried out and that by now the babies must have been devoured by wolves. And Dirce was delighted.

But all the while the children were growing up on Cithaeron in the care of the kind shepherd. He fed them on goat's milk and mountain honey, taught them to call him 'father' and named them Zethus and Amphion. And when they were old enough to begin to understand such things, he told them that their mother had been carried off by bandits and he no longer knew if she were alive or dead.

Up there in the hills, Zethus and Amphion grew into fine young men. Although they were twins, and one might have expected them to be very much alike, in fact they developed into two completely different individuals. Zethus became broad-shouldered and powerful, a truly heroic figure of a man. He loved hunting, and not even the most ferocious prey could make him quail. Amphion, by contrast, was musical and poetic. He would lead the flocks out to graze by the notes of his lyre, then sit on the mountain slopes for hours on end, playing and singing. So lovely were his melodies that they touched the hearts of the birds that heard them and tamed the savage spirits of the wildest beasts. Such was the power of Amphion's art that it could move the very stones around him.

Yet however much the young men differed, in one respect they were very much alike: in kindness of heart. Not only did they love each other dearly, but were united in affection for the shepherd they believed to be their father.

Twenty years had now gone by. And while Zethus and Amphion had grown up into fine young men, Antiope was still languishing in her vile prison and Dirce continued to enjoy the royal privileges she thought were hers for ever.

But in fact the wheel of time had turned full circle at last. For Zeus had never forgotten that in the end he must help his children, and that the throne of Thebes was theirs by right. And so one day, without any warning, the heavy bars fell from the door of Antiope's dungeon, it opened of its own accord, and the shackles dropped from her wrists. The twins' mother was finally free.

Bewildered, she staggered to her feet, went over to the

door and peered nervously out. There was not a soul in sight. This gave her the courage she needed, and with all the strength her frail limbs could command, backed by the power lent to her by hope, she fled straight to Cithaeron to hide from the avenging fury of Dirce. And what should happen but that her wild flight brought her to the very place where her children lived!

The shepherd was alone in the hut. She begged his help, revealed who she was and told him of her dreadful sufferings. Soon Zethus and Amphion came. The poor shepherd struggled to control his feelings, for he knew that before him an unhappy mother stood face to face with her lost children without knowing who they were. But he said nothing. Long ago he had given his promise, and now he must keep it. "Who knows what new ills may fall on Thebes if I reveal my secret?" the shepherd said to himself – and at that very moment a furious queen Dirce burst into the hut.

"Vile wretch!" she screamed. "Prison was the home the gods condemned you to. The time has come for you to die!"

And she immediately ordered Zethus and his brother to tie Antiope to the horns of a wild bull and let it tear her to pieces.

"She is guilty of hideous crimes," the queen went on. "I should have had her put to death long ago instead of keeping her in prison. She thought she could escape, but see how the gods have brought me to her and placed her in my hands and given me two fine young lads like you to punish her as she deserves."

Zethus and Amphion looked at their feet and said nothing.

"Move!" screeched Dirce. "Do you not hear me? The queen of Thebes commands you. Do as I say! Obey my command – for it is the will of the gods as well!"

With heavy hearts, the twins laid reluctant hands on the unknown woman who was their mother, not knowing how they could avoid the vile deed. But as they did so, the shepherd jumped to his feet crying:

"Miserable boys! Do you know who you have been ordered to kill? Your own mother, the former princess of Thebes!"

"Lies!" shrieked Dirce, but by way of answer the shepherd opened a trunk and took out the basket in which the boys had been brought to Cithaeron. The tiny garments they had worn were still inside.

"My sons!" sobbed Antiope, and rushed to embrace them.

"Treason!" hissed Dirce, turning on her heel.

"My troops will deal with this!"

But there was strength in the old shepherd yet, and he seized her arm in a grip of steel, crying out to the two young men:

"Now it is I who command! Take this woman and inflict on her the punishment she ordered for an innocent – your mother!"

Then Zethus and Amphion seized Dirce and bound her to the horns of the bull. And she was torn to pieces.

When justice had been done, the shepherd turned to the twins and said:

"My sons, this is the last time I can call you by that name, for I am not your father. As for your real father, your mother can reveal his name to you. The time has come for your return to Thebes, where the throne of Cadmus awaits you. Throw down the tyrant Lycus and set the city free. This is my final counsel as the father you believed me all these years. Go now, with my blessing. I shall remain here. For here I was born, here I grew to manhood, here I have reached old age, and here I wish to die."

And so Zethus and Amphion took their mother and went down into the city, where they overthrew the tyrant Lycus and became kings of Thebes.

The first task which faced them there was the fortification of the town. Cadmus had built walls, but only for Cadmea, the upper city, on its defensive spur of rock, and since his day the town which lay at its feet had grown considerably. Now new walls were needed, to enfold the whole of Thebes within their circuit.

Zethus and Amphion buckled down to the task. But just as they were unalike in other ways, so their methods of building differed immensely. Zethus used his titanic strength to heave huge boulders into place with his bare hands, but Amphion built in a strange and very different fashion. He simply played his lyre. And they say that such was the power of his music that the stones lifted themselves, at its command and fell into place, row upon row. Thus, with strength of hand and magic notes, the two brothers raised the mighty walls of the city which came to be known as Seven-Gated Thebes, after the seven tall gateways set in its impregnable circuit.

Zethus and Amphion ruled over the city in harmony and brotherly love, but they were not destined to live out their days in happiness.

Zethus married Aedon, and they had one child, a boy. But later, Aedon went mad and killed her child. Afterwards, she mourned for it ceaselessly, night and day, until at last the cruel loss of her son was more than she could bear and she died of grief. The gods took pity on her and transformed her into a nightingale and ever afterwards, Zethus awoke at dawn to the sad and lonely song of a bird.

Amphion married Niobe, the daughter of Tantalus. They lived in happiness for many years and produced fourteen children, and yet...

But that brings us to the last and one of the most tragic stories in this volume: the myth of Niobe.

THE PRIDE OF NIOBE

The tale of Niobe is not only the most dramatic but perhaps the most daring in the whole of Greek mythology. For like the myths of Prometheus and Deucalion's Flood it poses a very bold and direct question: why are the gods so often unjust to mortals?

Niobe may have been at fault, but she was punished so harshly and inhumanly that whatever crime she was guilty of pales before the vengeance that was wreaked on her. The sentence passed on Niobe becomes a condemnation of the gods themselves.

As the wife of Amphion and the mother of so many children, Niobe was the happiest woman in the world – until the day disaster struck. She was a queen, her husband loved her dearly, but above all she had her fourteen children, seven boys and seven girls, all as fair as young gods and the pride and joy of her heart.

Niobe's children were her whole existence. She washed and combed them with her own hands, fed the younger ones, and rejoiced in the handsome and united family she and her husband had brought into the world.

To be proud of one's family is no crime – as long as one does not make hurtful comparisons. But in her pride, Niobe did make such a comparison, and in so doing she insulted no less a person than a goddess.

"I am the best and happiest mother on earth," Niobe would often say. "Not only on earth, but in the heavens, too." Until one day her old nurse said to her:

"But, madam, the story our parents and our grandparents always told us was that the best and happiest of mothers is the goddess Leto, who bore Apollo and Artemis, both mighty gods respected by mortals and immortals alike."

"I have borne fourteen such children," was Niobe's proud response. "My sons are a match for the finest athletes, and brilliant horsemen. My daughters are the fairest flowers of

Thebes, and the seven great towers of the city walls bear their names. So how could Leto, with a mere two children, be a better mother than me?"

"You may be queen," the nurse replied, "but once you were just a child at my breast, and that gives me the right to chide you. Take those words back! Be as proud as you like among mortals, but be humble before the gods. For their power is beyond all reckoning, and we are as nothing beside them."

"Others are nothing, perhaps, but not I."

"Madam, watch your tongue!"

"I am the darling of the gods, and my fourteen children give me my power. My shield is my husband, king of Thebes and son of Zeus!"

"Alas, my lady, if only the gods could not hear the words of mortals and read their thoughts, then perhaps no harm would come to you. But now I am afraid, very afraid. I fear disaster, madam."

Sure enough, Leto did learn what Niobe had said, and her rage was terrible to see. She immediately summoned the soothsayer Manto, daughter of the prophet Tiresias, and commanded her:

"Go now to Thebes and order the mothers of the city to make humble sacrifice to me. And be sure that not a single one of them fails to pay heed, for the vengeance that will fall on her will be hideous beyond all imagining."

Manto hastened to Thebes and proclaimed the goddess'

command in every corner of the city, and below the palace walls as well. As soon as they heard her words every mother in the town hastily offered sacrifice to Leto. All except Niobe, who remained stubbornly in the palace.

"Go, your majesty," the old nurse begged. "Go before disaster sfrikes. Go now, for soon it will be too late!"

"I do not fear Leto," was the queen's reply. "I have never humbled myself before, and I shall not do so now. I have fourteen children and I am the better mother. I'll offer no sacrifice to her!"

And she did not.

Then Leto called her children to her, the two unerring archers Apollo and Artemis, and in a voice trembling with rage she told them of the terrible insult she had been subjected to. And then she added:

"If Niobe is not punished, men will cease to revere me, and I shall no longer be worshipped as a goddess. My altars will be left to crumble and I shall go unheeded by the other gods."

"Fear not, mother," was Apollo's reply. "We shall allow no mortal woman to humiliate you, whoever she may be. We know what you seek of us, and we shall carry out the deed."

"Come, brother!" cried Artemis, "and we shall see how many children that upstart has left to her name before very long. We'll teach her to insult a goddess – especially our mother!"

The pair of them set off for Thebes at once, their quivers bristling with the deadly arrows which warned of the catastrophe to come.

When they reached the city, all the young men of Thebes were taking part in athletics contests at the foot of the castle walls. And in every event, Niobe's seven fine sons stood out from the other competitors.

Wrapped in a concealing cloud, Apollo seated himself on a rock high up on the acropolis. His keen eye soon made out Niobe's seven sons. Next, he took seven arrows from his quiver and laid them at his side. Then, after another careful look at the stadium below, he picked up an arrow and took aim. The missile winged its way earthwards with a shrill whine, followed by Apollo's steady gaze. And it found its mark: one of the athletes fell lifeless to the ground. Then he took another arrow, and a third, and a fourth, until seven fine young men lay stretched out dead in the dust.

And so, in the hour when victors should be praised, the people of Thebes found themselves mourning their dead, and instead of a procession led by laurel-crowned champions, a funeral cortege made its solemn way to the palace, bearing the bodies of the city's seven finest youths.

As they came up the hill, Amphion stood waiting at the castle gate, as he always did, to offer his congratulations to the victors. But the procession which approached him now was like no other he remembered. He gazed in growing anxiety as the long column drew nearer, silent and mournful. Thoughts of some dreadful disaster were already turning over in his mind, but none so dreadful as that which greeted him as he saw laid out before him on the ground, one by one, the bodies of all his seven sons.

Amphion's eyes beheld the sight, but for a long moment his mind could not take it in. And when at last he had fully comprehended the horror of what lay before him, he raised his eyes to the heavens and a silent cry of anguish tore his heart asunder. Then his head dropped, his eyes fired with despairing wrath and his hand went to his sword-hilt. A moment later, with dreadful suddenness, he plunged the blade into his own breast.

As Amphion sank lifeless to the ground, Niobe and her seven daughters appeared in the gateway.

With heartrending cries of grief the girls threw themselves on the bodies of their murdered brothers and their beloved father.

Only Niobe remained standing. Unable to bear the hideous sight, she hid her head in her hands. Although she managed to hold back the sobs which were choking her, she could not prevent the tears from streaming down her face. She saw that the disaster they had warned her of had struck, and an agonizing struggle was now taking place inside her. For even this inhuman punishment could not bow the queen's proud spirit. In her heart of hearts she could never accept that Leto was a better mother than she, or that by this blow she had established her superiority.

And so, drawing on whatever reserves of courage were left within her, Niobe wiped the tears from her cheeks, lifted her arms heavenwards and cried:

"Leto! May your soul rejoice in the hideous crime you have committed. Let it exult in the triumph of your cruelty – but do not think this is a victory, Leto. However many lifeless corpses lie scattered around me, I still have my seven daughters to sweeten my sorrow. Oh yes, I have always been a better mother than you, and I still am. You shall never be my equal!"

All who heard Niobe froze at her words. Blinded by her pride, could she not see that her rash cry was yet another challenge to the goddess, and one that would surely not go unanswered?

And a moment later the shrill whine of an arrow drew their eyes like a magnet towards one of Niobe's daughters: transfixed by the deadly shaft, she was already gasping out her life above her brother's body.

For now Artemis had taken up where Apollo had laid down his bow. One by one, her swift, sure arrows tore into the hearts of Niobe's daughters. Six of the seven already lay dead and now only one was left – little Chloris, the youngest and dearest of the unhappy queen's beloved daughters.

In this last moment, surrounded by the heartrending evidence of the gods' inconceivable harshness, Niobe's pride collapsed. Wild with grief, she threw herself on her knees, turned her eyes heavenwards and cried out in a voice broken with anguish:

"O great and mighty Leto! You have defeated me! Forgive me for insulting you, take pity on my misery, and, I beg you, I implore you: let me keep the last of my little ones to soften my grief!"

Niobe writhed in her misery. Again and again she threw herself to the ground, stretching her hands towards the heavens and beating her breast in supplication.

"If you cannot take pity on me, at least show mercy on this harmless creature. Kill me, but let her live: to cry, to forget, to bow her knee before your mighty name!"

Niobe had now humbled herself utterly before Leto. The last shreds of her self-esteem had fallen from her, and the goddess was delighted. But she was not moved to pity. Niobe's cries would have melted a heart of ice, but they did not soften Leto's rage. A brief and vicious whine rang through the air and the last of Artemis' arrows buried itself in the last of Niobe's daughters. She died in her mother's arms.

The queen stood among the gods' cruel handiwork a creature dazed with grief. All her children lay dead. Her husband, too. Even little Chloris. The slaughter was beyond belief, too terrible for words – but unalterably real. Her pride and happiness in ruins, Niobe no longer even had the strength to cry.

..."O great and mighty Leto! I beg you, I implore you: let
me keep the last of my little ones to soften my grief!"...

Speechless and dry-mouthed, she remained there in her sorrow as if all life had fled from her body, and only the tears which flowed down her cheeks bore witness to her unendurable pain.

Then suddenly her ears were pierced by a hideous and rasping voice. The gods had not yet had their fill of revenge. The soothsayer Manto was making her rounds again, crying shrilly in every quarter of the city:

"Hear my words, people of Thebes! The immortal gods forbid you to bury the children of Niobe. To increase this vain woman's punishment and to teach every man and woman in this town the true might of the gods, the bodies of Niobe's children will go unburied and be eaten by the birds of prey."

Again and again the prophetess shrieked out her message, until Niobe could endure no more. The warm and living queen slowly turned into a block of stone. Soon, all that remained of her loving spirit were the tears that flowed from her stone eyes and the anguish which swelled within her stone heart.

And as that anguish swelled, so did the stone figure of Niobe, until it towered over the rooftops of Thebes, a looming accusation against the injustice of the immortals.

When the gods beheld that rising pillar of rock, and saw the tears which still flowed from Niobe's stone eyes to reproach them for their hideous revenge, they at last comprehended the evil they had done, and were filled first with shame and then with fear.

As if they knew now that theirs was no victory, but a humiliating defeat, they came secretly in the night and buried Niobe's children with their own hands. And then, raising a fearful whirlwind, they lifted the rock and bore it far away into the depths of Asia, where they hid it behind Mount Sipylus in the hope that the cruel act they had committed might thus be forgotten.

But it was not forgotten. Thousands of years have gone by and men still recount the myth of Niobe, for all the efforts of the gods to hide their crime.

For it was not mere chance that gave birth to this tale.

On the far slopes of Mount Sipylus one can still see a rock which weeps with the melting of the snows, and bears some resemblance to a sorrowing woman. However, could such a rock alone have given rise to a myth like this? Perhaps some terrible disaster really did befall the royal house of Thebes, a disaster which provoked a universal outrage which in its turn gave birth to the myth. From then on it is merely a question of imagination and reasoning – but logical and bold reasoning, so bold that it places mortals and immortals, Mankind and Olympians, in opposing camps. For here the gods are judged, and found guilty of a crime so monstrous it outreaches the powers of justice; while mortal men, in the person of Niobe, raise up against it the strong rock built of all their sufferings, a rock so enduring it can outlast the gods themselves.

For whatever else may be true, this much is certain:

Somewhere on the face of this earth there is such a rock, shaped like a tragic but still proud woman who seems to be sending heavenwards a mute yet eloquent cry of accusation. Try as they might, storms and tempests cannot muffle this cry, and neither can the passing of the centuries.

And on Olympus? Up there, there is nothing. Nothing but bare and silent crags, scoured by the icy winds. The halls of the gods are as if they had never been.

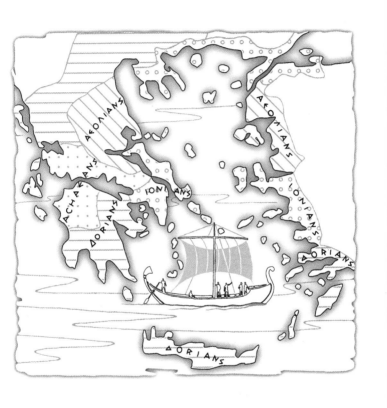